DIRECTORY of illustration 26 GET BIG!

PUBLISHER / EDITOR
Glen R. Serbin

VICE PRESIDENT / SOURCE BOOK DIRECTOR
Elizabeth Nebb Owen

CONTROLLER
Mai Raack

MARKETING REPRESENTATIVES
Ellie Altomare
Adrian Johnson
Jo Ann Miller
Beth Pierson

DIRECTOR OF PRODUCTION
Tamra Dempsey

PRODUCTION MANAGER
Barbara Kuhn

PRODUCTION STAFF
Keane Roberts

PAGE DESIGN SERVICES
Theil Shelton

DISTRIBUTION COORDINATOR
Christiane Laberge Hitchcock

PROOFING
Karen Bridgers
Julie Simpson

ACCOUNTING ASSISTANT
Johanna Wagner

MANAGING EDITOR / MAGAZINE DIVISION
Julie Simpson

MANAGER / SITEDESIGNWORKS DIVISION
Christina Henson

ADMINISTRATIVE SUPPORT
Kim Taylor

ACCOUNTING FIRM
Damitz, Brooks, Nightingale,
Turner & Morrisset

PRINTER
Toppan Printing Co., Ltd.

SHIPPING & MAILING
Express Logistics, Inc.

BOOK DESIGN & ART DIRECTION
Spur Design

COVER & INTERIOR ILLUSTRATIONS
Aaron Meshon
www.aaronmeshon.com
see pages 298-299

PUBLISHED BY
Serbin Communications, Inc.
813 Reddick Street
Santa Barbara, California 93103
805-963-0439
www.serbin.com
email: info@serbin.com

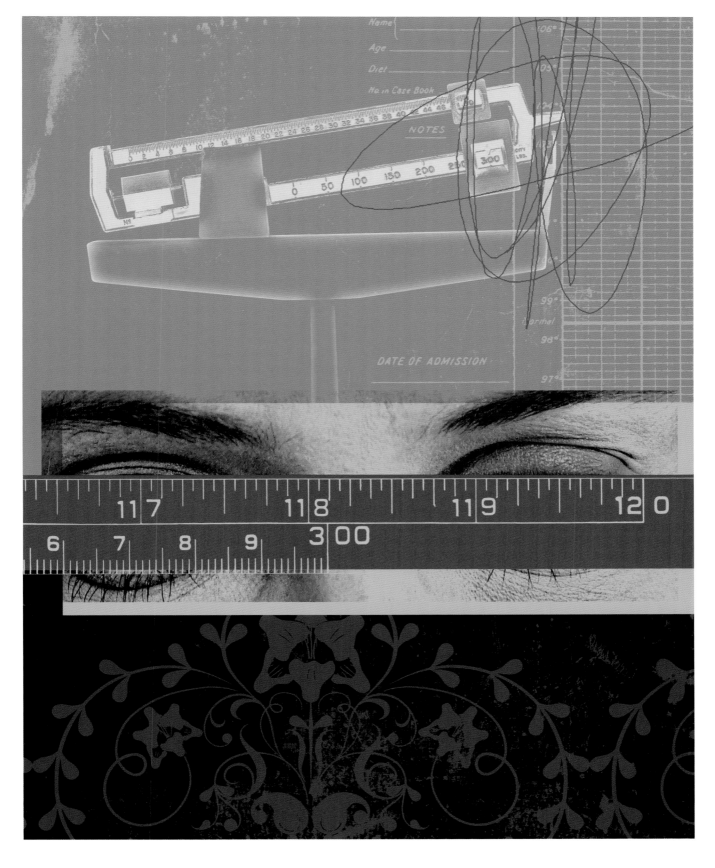

michele MELCHER

ralph **VOLTZ**

simon SHAW

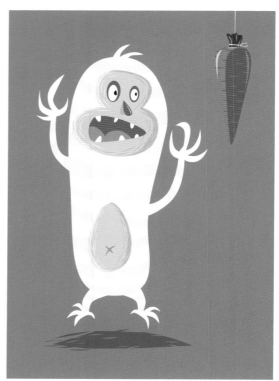

Practice Saying No!

WON'T YOU HEAD THE PICNIC COMMITTEE?

PLEASE?

I FEEL BAD LETTING THEM DOWN, BUT...

THAT'S A BIG JOB AND I PROMISED MYSELF TIME TO GARDEN THIS YEAR...

I'M SORRY, I'M NOT ABLE TO LEAD THE PROJECT.

I'LL MAKE CUPCAKES.

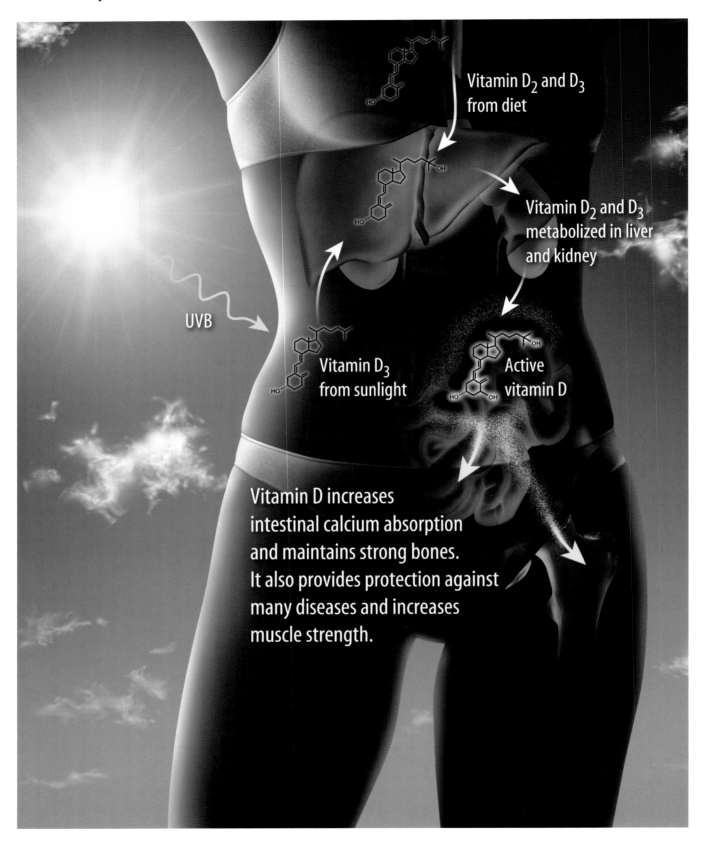

Vitamin D$_2$ and D$_3$ from diet

Vitamin D$_2$ and D$_3$ metabolized in liver and kidney

UVB

Vitamin D$_3$ from sunlight

Active vitamin D

Vitamin D increases intestinal calcium absorption and maintains strong bones. It also provides protection against many diseases and increases muscle strength.

215.232.6666   www.illustrationOnLine.com   **DEBORAH WOLFE LTD**

215.232.6666   www.illustrationOnLine.com   **DEBORAH WOLFE LTD**

dan McGEEHAN

john SCHREINER

38

b|A

Bernstein & Andriulli
212-682-1490
artinfo@ba-reps.com
www.ba-reps.com

[TRISTAN EATON]
www.thunderdogstudios.com

B·BOT
for the iPhone

BERNSTEIN & ANDRIULLI   WWW.BA-REPS.COM
ARTINFO@BA-REPS.COM   212-682-1490

MARY ANN LASHER

BERNSTEIN & ANDRIULLI   WWW.BA-REPS.COM
ARTINFO@BA-REPS.COM   212-682-1490

BERNSTEIN & ANDRIULLI   WWW.BA-REPS.COM
ARTINFO@BA-REPS.COM   212-682-1490

BERNSTEIN & ANDRIULLI   WWW.BA-REPS.COM
ARTINFO@BA-REPS.COM   212-682-1490

BERNSTEIN & ANDRIULLI   WWW.BA-REPS.COM
ARTINFO@BA-REPS.COM   212-682-1490

BERNSTEIN & ANDRIULLI   WWW.BA-REPS.COM
ARTINFO@BA-REPS.COM   212-682-1490

BERNSTEIN & ANDRIULLI   WWW.BA-REPS.COM
ARTINFO@BA-REPS.COM   212-682-1490

ALETA RAFTON

BERNSTEIN & ANDRIULLI   WWW.BA-REPS.COM
ARTINFO@BA-REPS.COM   212-682-1490

BERNSTEIN & ANDRIULLI   WWW.BA-REPS.COM
ARTINFO@BA-REPS.COM   212-682-1490

BERNSTEIN & ANDRIULLI   WWW.BA-REPS.COM
ARTINFO@BA-REPS.COM   212-682-1490

BERNSTEIN & ANDRIULLI   WWW.BA-REPS.COM
ARTINFO@BA-REPS.COM   212-682-1490

JEFF NISHINAKA

Photography by Bela Borsodi

Photography by PSC Photography

BERNSTEIN & ANDRIULLI   WWW.BA-REPS.COM
ARTINFO@BA-REPS.COM   212-682-1490

LEONELLO CALVETTI

BERNSTEIN & ANDRIULLI   WWW.BA-REPS.COM
ARTINFO@BA-REPS.COM   212-682-1490

KANO

TES ONE

BERNSTEIN & ANDRIULLI   WWW.BA-REPS.COM
ARTINFO@BA-REPS.COM   212-682-1490

SAM HADLEY

TIM MARRS

BERNSTEIN & ANDRIULLI   WWW.BA-REPS.COM
ARTINFO@ba-reps.com   212-682-1490

BERNSTEIN & ANDRIULLI   WWW.BA-REPS.COM
ARTINFO@BA-REPS.COM   212-682-1490

www.aareps.com

ANIMATION

INTERACTIVE

CGI

ILLUSTRATION

FLASH

PHOTOGRAPHY

AA REPS
American Artists Representatives

ph.212.682.2462
fx.212.582.0090
info@aareps.com

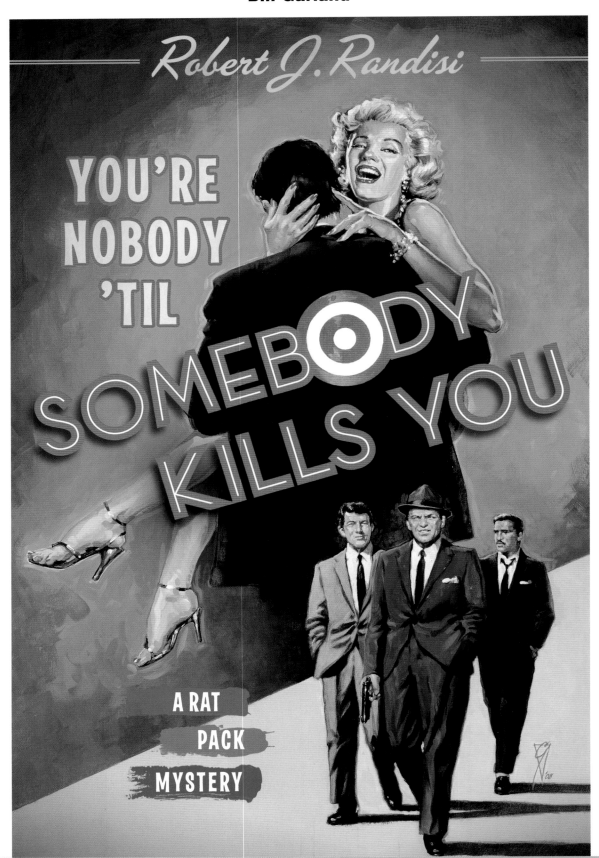

Jerry LoFaro

Original Prescription Strength

NEW!
Non-Drowsy*
Claritin®
Loratadine 10 mg/Antihistamine

**24 hour
Allergy**

Relief of:
Sneezing; Runny Nose
Itchy, Watery Eyes
Itchy Throat or Nose

5 Tablets

Actual Size

* When taken as directed. See Drug Facts Panel.

American Artists Representatives

AA REPS
creative solutions since the 1920's

Shawn McKelvey

Kathleen A. Hurwitz M.D.

Illustrated by Shawn Mc Kel

Frank Neidhardt

Curt Walstead

Tony Randazzo

Kent Gamble

Mike Bryan

Alan Male

Geo Parkin

TRG
REALITY

WHETHER IT'S A SIMPLE RENDERING OF A PRODUCT THAT DOESN'T YET EXIST OR A WEIGHT LIFTING DUCK, WE HAVE THE CAPABILITY TO PRODUCE WORK THAT WOULDN'T BE ACHIEVABLE BY ORDINARY MEANS AND ORDINARY BUDGETS.

COMPOSITING PROCESS...

STUDIO PHOTO   CGI WIREFRAME   MAGIC   RENDERED IMAGE

American Artists Representatives

AA REPS
creative solutions since the 1920's

Find Your Solution
www.aareps.com
www.aarepsinteractive.com

ph. 212.682.2462
info@aareps.com

Bob Wakelin

Fiammetta Dogi

Chris Hopkins

Mike Jaroszko

David Semple

Andrew Painter

Phil Howe

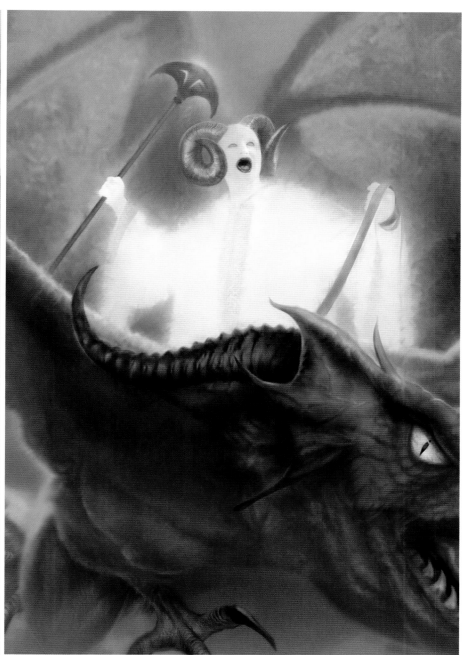

Jon Rogers

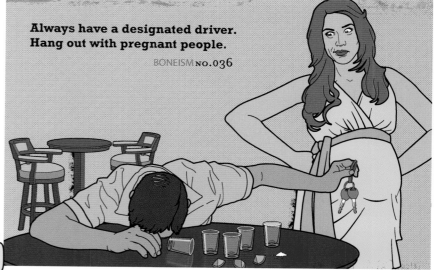

Always have a designated driver.
Hang out with pregnant people.

BONEISM no. 036

DELAY OF GAME

OFFSIDE

HOLDING

ILLEGAL USE OF HANDS

UNSPORTSMANLIKE CONDUCT

PASS INTERFERENCE

ROUGHING THE PASSER

HORSE COLLAR

Marc Mones

Mark Snyder

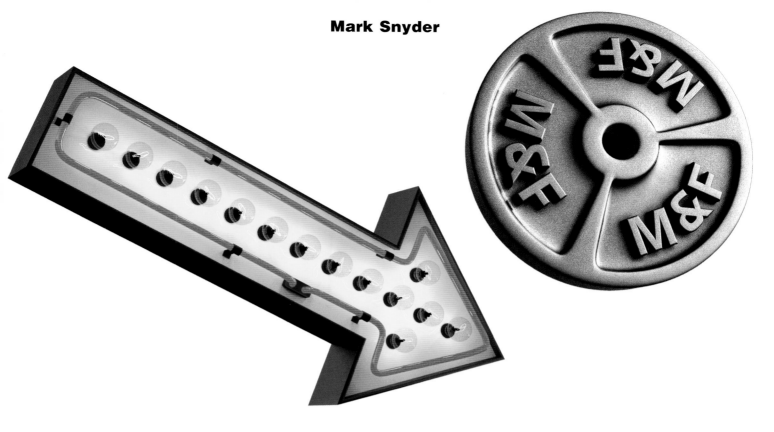

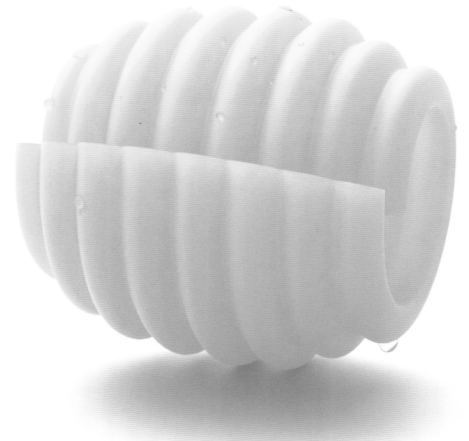

Garth Glazier

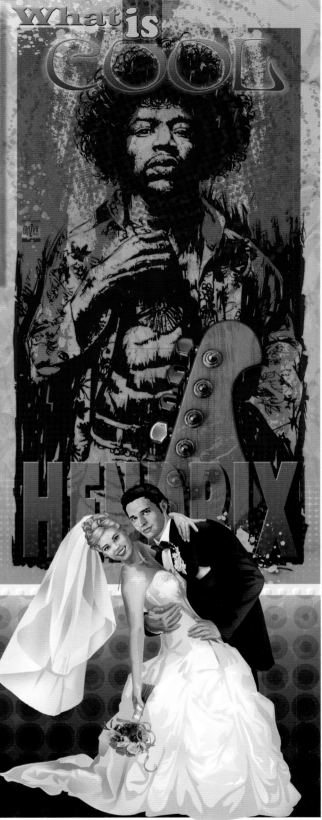

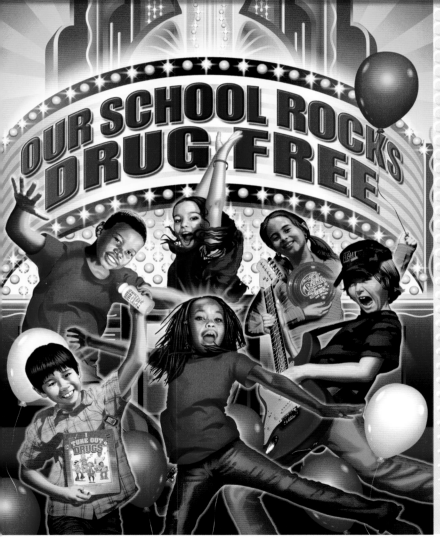

RIVE GAUCHE
STUDIO

Marcel Laverdet

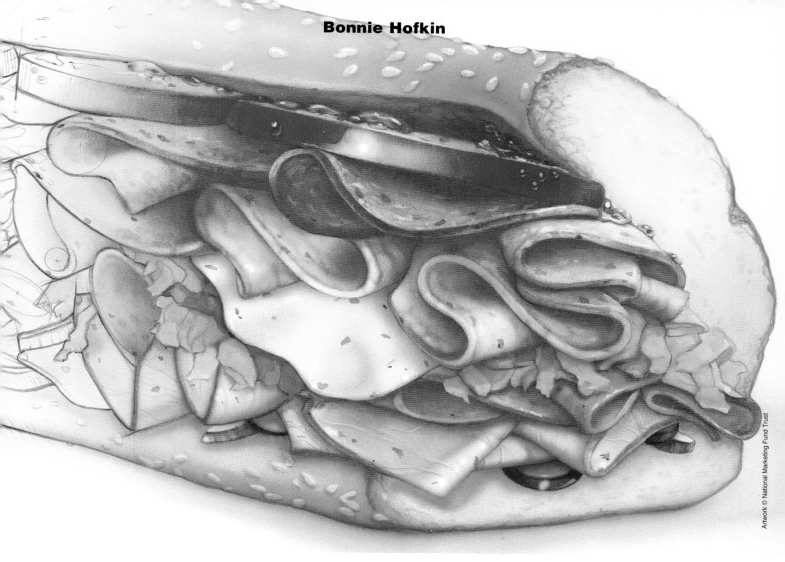

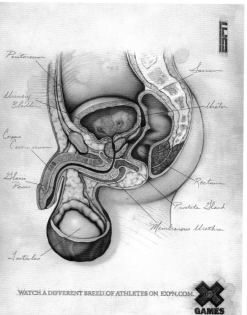

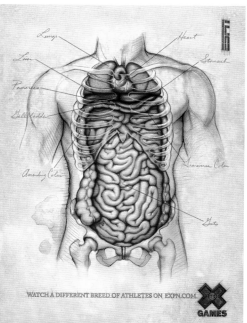

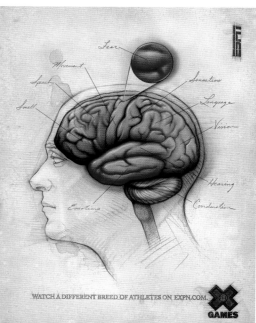

WATCH A DIFFERENT BREED OF ATHLETES ON EXPN.COM.

X GAMES

Craig Zuckerman

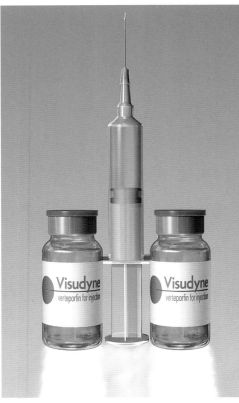

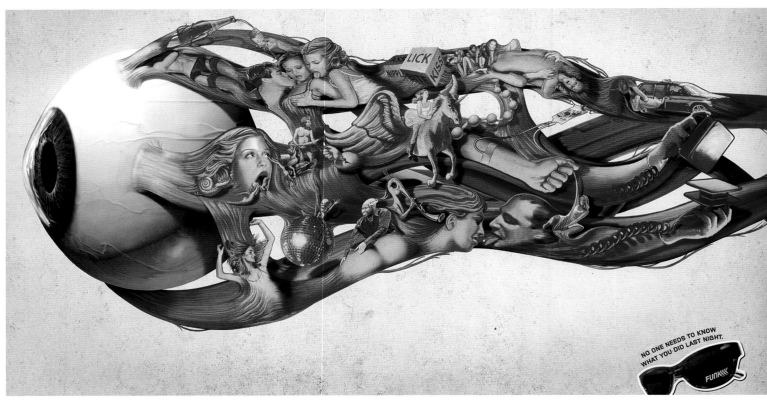

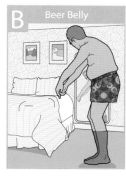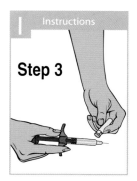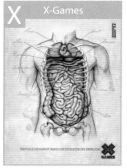
99

JAMES YANG is proudly represented by DAVID GOLDMAN AGENCY
p: 212-807-6627 • **www.davidgoldmanagency.com** • dg@davidgoldmanagency.com

LINDA DAVICK is proudly represented by DAVID GOLDMAN AGENCY
p: 212-807-6627 · **www.davidgoldmanagency.com** · dg@davidgoldmanagency.com

STEVE DININNO is proudly represented by DAVID GOLDMAN AGENCY
p: 212-807-6627 • **www.davidgoldmanagency.com** • dg@davidgoldmanagency.com

PHIL DISLEY is proudly represented by DAVID GOLDMAN AGENCY
p: 212-807-6627 • **www.davidgoldmanagency.com** • dg@davidgoldmanagency.com

REPRESENTING THE WORLD'S FINEST ILLUSTRATORS, PHOTOGRAPHERS & WRITERS FOR OVER 20 YEARS.

630 Ninth Avenue, Suite 707
New York, New York 10036
Telephone: 215.333.2551

A.K.A.

MICHAEL KOELSCH

SHANNONASSOCIATES.COM

YUCEL

PABLO BERNASCONI

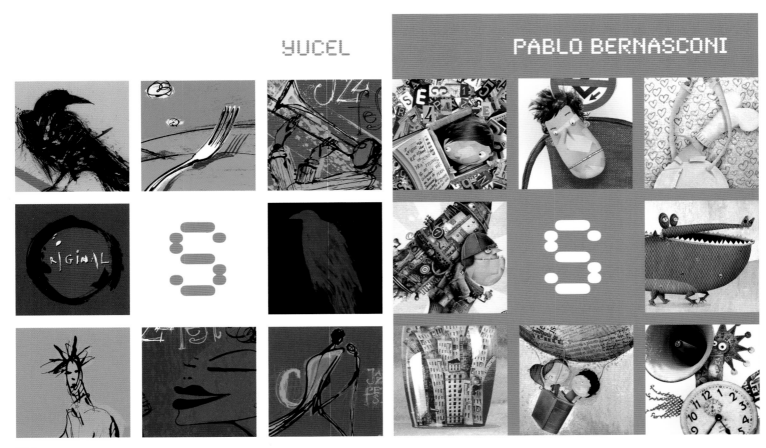

MURILO MACIEL

GUILHERME MARCONI

SHANNONASSOCIATES.COM

IAN KELTIE

SPORK UNLIMITED

JUSTIN BRANDSTATER

CHAD MICHAEL WARD

SHANNONASSOCIATES.COM

MARCOS CALO

STEVE JAMES

PETER BOLLINGER

DAVE SEELEY

SHANNONASSOCIATES.COM

CLIFF NIELSEN

MONIKA ROE

MELODY CASSEN

SHANE REBENSCHIED

SHANNONASSOCIATES.COM

BLAKE MORROW

ALI SMITH

DOUG HOLGATE

JOHN JAY

SHANNONASSOCIATES.COM

TIN SALAMUNIC

CRAIG PHILLIPS

MIKE LAUGHEAD

BILL MCGUIRE

SHANNONASSOCIATES.COM

RICARDO TERCIO

PAULE TRUDEL

OMAR RAYYAN

ROBERT HUNT

SHANNONASSOCIATES.COM

TRISTAN ELWELL

PATRICK FARICY

GLIN DIBLEY

STACY CURTIS

SHANNONASSOCIATES.COM

WILSON ONG

JOHN SHROADES

ANTONIO JAVIER CAPARO

MARK ELLIOTT

SHANNONASSOCIATES.COM

CHRIS BEATRICE

VINCENT NGUYEN

MARYN ROOS

UTE SIMON

SHANNONASSOCIATES.COM

SANTIAGO COHEN

SUSAN MITCHELL

NATHAN HALE

RICHARD COWDREY

SHANNONASSOCIATES.COM

PATRICIA CASTELAO

PETER BAY ALEXANDERSEN

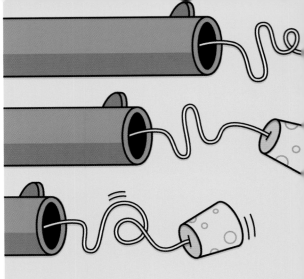

Harry Campbell

Represented by Gerald & Cullen Rapp 212-889-3337
www.rappart.com   info@rappart.com

Lonnie Busch   Gerald & Cullen Rapp   Lonnie Busch

212-889-3337
www.rappart.com
info@rappart.com

Cullen Rapp   Lonnie Busch   Gerald & Cullen Rapp

CELIA JOHNSON

GERALD & CULLEN RAPP
212 889 3337

info@rappart.com
www.rappart.com

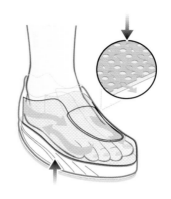

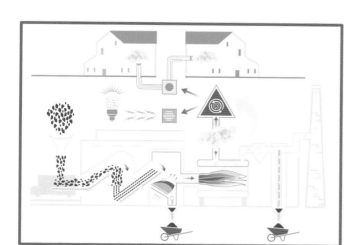

STEVE JOBS
NOBODY LOVES ME

MLB TEAM VALUES
BASEBALL'S BEST BOSS

MICROSOFT VS. GE
THE FIGHT OVER YOUR
MEDICAL RECORDS

MAY 11, 2009 | WWW.FORBES.COM

Forbes
SURVIVOR'S GUIDE
FOR THE AFFLUENT

Sean McCabe

GERALD & CULLEN RAPP
212 889 3337 / info@rappart.com
www.rappart.com / www.wider-than-pictures.com

Nigel Buchanan
Represented by
Gerald and Cullen Rapp
212.889.3337
info@rappart.com
www.rappart.com
www.nigelbuchanan.com

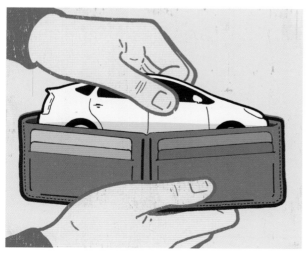

DAN PAGE
www.danpage.net

Gerald & Cullen Rapp . 212-889-3337 . info@rappart.com . www.rappart.com

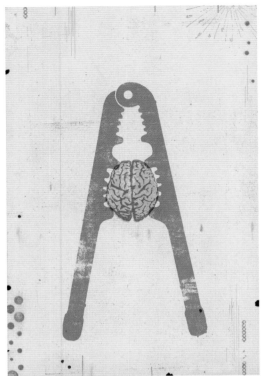

Richard Mia | www.richardmia.com | Gerald & Cullen Rapp | 212-889-3337 | info@rappart.com | www.rappart.com

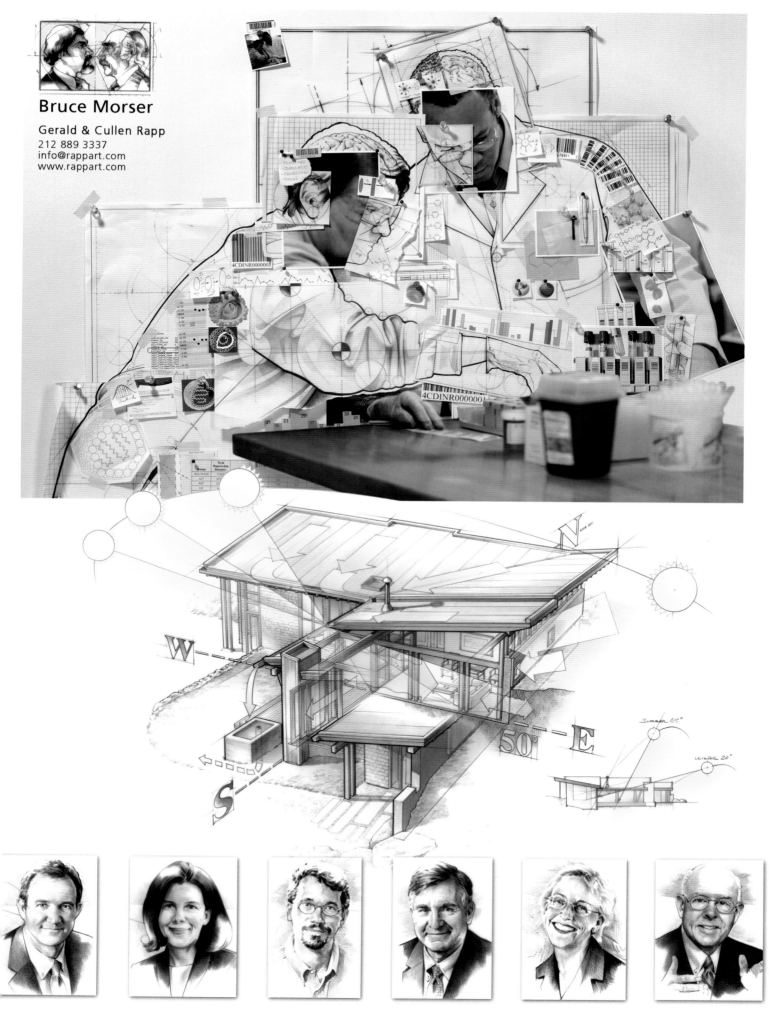

Bruce Morser

Gerald & Cullen Rapp
212 889 3337
info@rappart.com
www.rappart.com

Marc Rosenthal

represented by Gerald & Cullen Rapp 212-889-3337 info@rappart.com
www.rappart.com, www.marc-rosenthal.com

STEPHANIE DALTON COWAN

represented by: gerald & cullen rapp   212.889.3337   www.rappart.com   info@rappart.com   www.daltoncowan.com

CARA PETRUS ⟶ REPRESENTED BY GERALD & CULLEN RAPP

212-889-3337 ✳ INFO@RAPPART.COM ✳ WWW.RAPPART.COM

Mark Fredrickson
Gerald & Cullen Rapp
212-889-3337   www.rappart.com
info@rappart.com

Brian Ajhar

Gerald & Cullen Rapp
212 889 3337
info@rappart.com
www.rappart.com
www.ajhar.com

James Steinberg

Gerald & Cullen Rapp
212 889 3337
info@rappart.com
www.rappart.com
www.james-steinberg.com

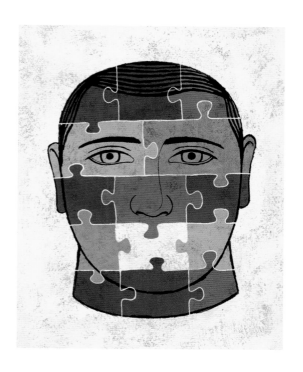

MENDOLA
ARTISTS REPRESENTATIVES

WWW.MENDOLAART.COM

PH 212.986.5680 | info@mendolaart.com

Russell Benfanti
www.benfanti.com

FORBIDDEN TO ALL
BUT A PRIVILEGED FEW

VITAMIN D - ATTACHES TO YOUR REGIMIN

OAKLEY

THE GEOGRAPHY OF LIGHT

HELP THEM HOLD ON TO THE MOMENT

PRILIGY

MENDOLA
ARTISTS REPRESENTATIVES

WWW.MENDOLAART.COM
PH 212.986.5680 | E mendolaart@aol.com

Dan Sipple Illustration
www.dansipple.com

2009 US OPEN

NEW YORK CITY
AUGUST 25 TO SEPTEMBER 7

US OPEN

A USTA EVENT

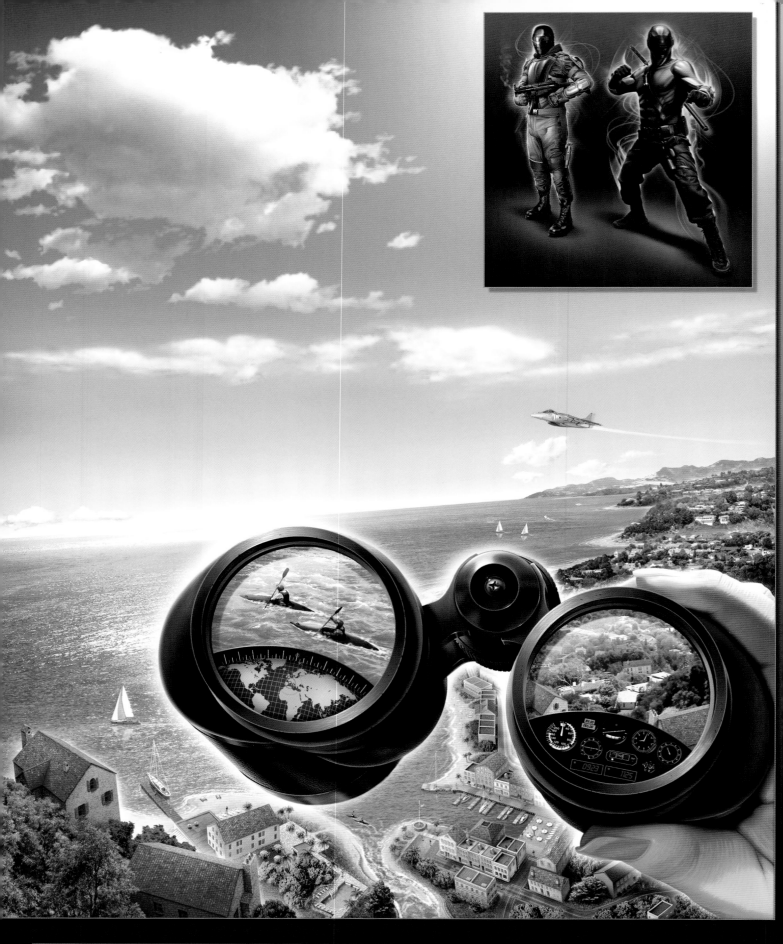

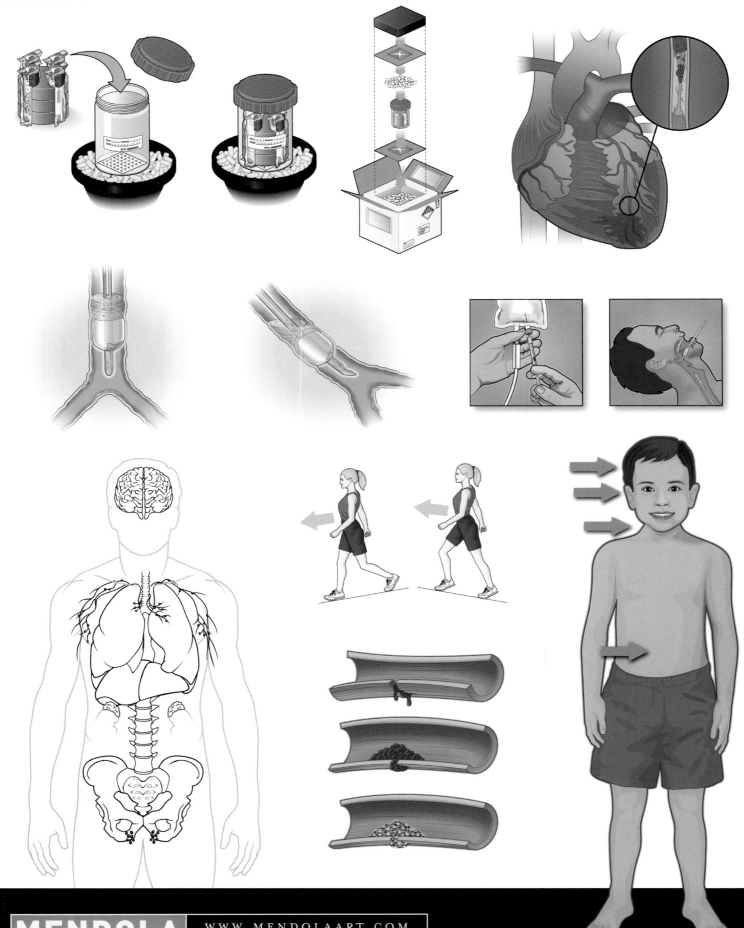

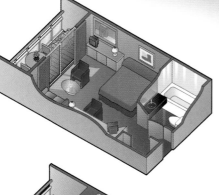

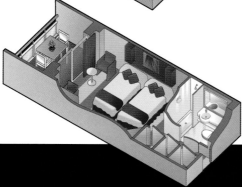

KOPP ILLUSTRATION

Skullcandy

MADE
IN HARMONY
WITH
NATURE

ROCK SHOX

IS THIS YOU

Family sedan with a dark side...

Ford

I ❤ living out-loud

Get the party started with the new Sony Ericsson W395.
With built-in stereo speakers so you can pump out your music
at the volume it deserves.

Sony Ericsson
Walkman

US OPEN
2009

US OPEN
A USTA EVENT

CLUE®

SECRETS IN PARIS

NATIONALE
POLICE
Aéroport
2009

CONFIDENTIAL
CLUE

France

Family 8+ | 3-6 PLAYERS

Solve the
MYSTERY
on the High School
CLASS TRIP!

Hasbro

Macmillan McGraw-Hill

Florida

Math Connects

Giraffa Laff Limbo

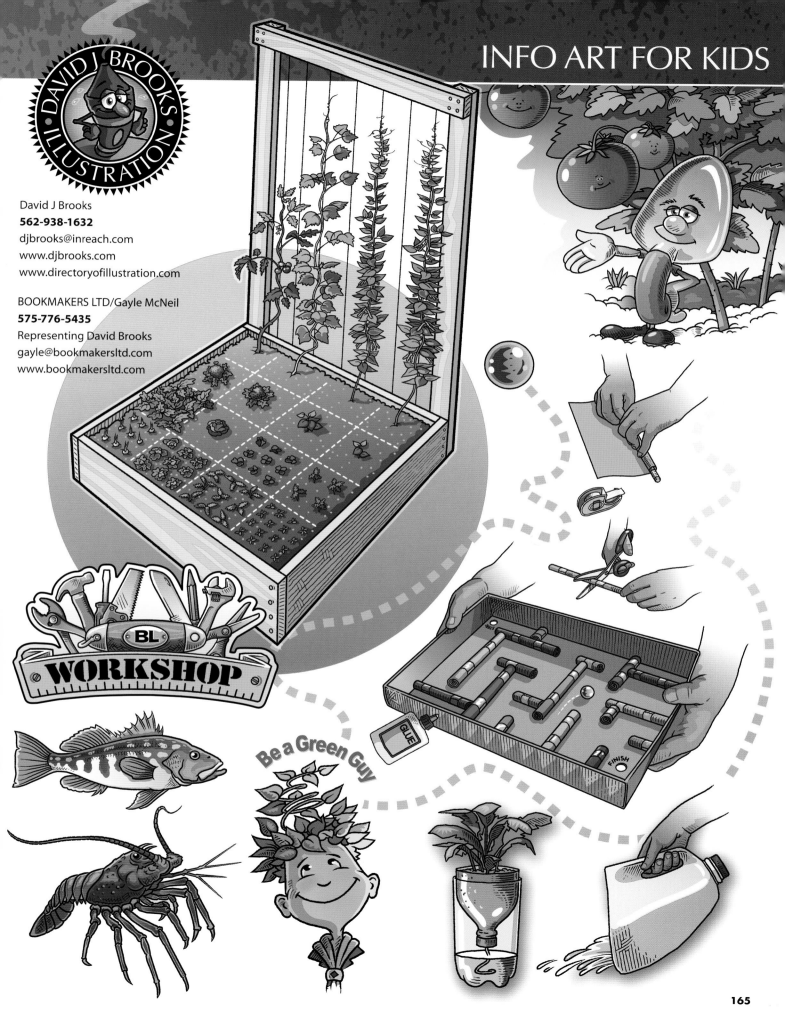

David J Brooks
562-938-1632
djbrooks@inreach.com
www.djbrooks.com
www.directoryofillustration.com

BOOKMAKERS LTD/Gayle McNeil
575-776-5435
Representing David Brooks
gayle@bookmakersltd.com
www.bookmakersltd.com

Be a Green Guy

JOHN PARRA
www.johnparraart.com

PAULA GOODMAN KOZ

www.paulagoodmankoz.com

Shakespeare's "The Winter's Tale" is a late, mellow work. The idea of a snowglobe first came to me because of the word "winter". Along with music boxes, carousels and kaleidoscopes, snowglobes make me feel nostalgic by reminding me of memory, the past, and childhood. I put young Florizel and Perdita inside a snowglobe in order to keep them safe--as does Shakespeare in his lovely play. I specialize in color and black-and-white woodcuts and linocuts. A recent client list includes Mondo Publishing, NewSouth Books, Inc., National Public Radio (2009 Calendar) and Virginia Shakespeare Festival (VSF). © 2009 - Young Prince Florizel and Perdita

PETE PASPALOVSKI

www.prespastudios.com

"Before the first brushstroke, I thoroughly research my subject to ensure historical accuracy. After a collaborative discussion with the client the models are chosen as a casting director would choose an actor. My main influences are the works of Caravaggio and Rembrandt. This portrait evokes the classic American cowboy with lean chiseled features, a strong look, but with a hint of sadness and loneliness. There is also a hint of patriotism hidden in the red white and blue colors used for the handkerchief, the highlights and the eyes. Some of Pete's clients include Great Lakes Publishing, Schwebels, Detroit Jazz Fest, Latina Magazine and Julius Zorn Inc. © 2009 - The Cowboy

CHRIS BUZELLI

BOB DOB

RACHEL SALOMON

MARTHA RICH

JENVAUGHNART.COM

415.666.3447

ELLIOTT GOLDEN

CLAUDINE HELLMUTH

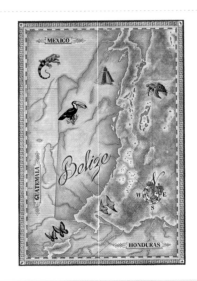

DAVE STEVENSON

ROBIN MOLINE

170

TERRI FRY KASUBA

HANNAH STOUFFER

JEN LOBO

JOEL NAKAMURA

JENVAUGHNART.COM

415.666.3447

CHARLES GLAUBITZ

CALEF BROWN

OMAR LEE

CRAIG LA ROTONDA

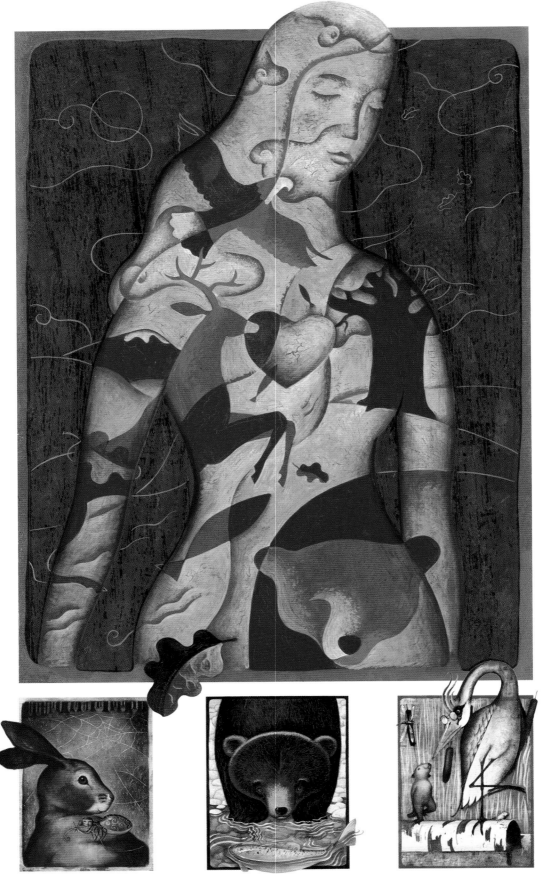

From the book,"The Wandering Wonderings Of Little Bear"

keith *skeen*

Stacy Peterson

Stacy Peterson
Represented by Langley Creative 321-782 0244
s.langley@langleycreative.com / j.blasco@langleycreative.com
www.langleycreative.com www.stacypeterson.net

Agents:
Stacey Endress
Juliette Lott
Victoria Pearce
Nina Goldberger
Richard Watkins
Mike Cowley
Harry Lyon-Smith

Ben Tallon

Illustration

23 Ohio Street
Maplewood
NJ 07040
1-8886-ILLUSTRATION
us@illustrationweb.com

Representing the world's leading illustrators since 1929

AT Rock

Koichi Fujii

Dishman

Ella Tjader

Andrew Selby

Ami Plasse

Kat Cameron

Christopher Corr

Ruth Rowland

Hannah Firmin

Hydrangeas have become part of the furniture, but don't let familiarity bre contempt, says **Rae Spencer-Jones** takes a fresh look at this old favourite

Erica Burns

Nuno Da Costa

Nadia Flower

Daria Jabenko

Sonya Suhariyan

Sarah Beetson

Wai

Adam Lowe

Emma Rios

Jacqueline Bissett

Montana Forbes

Dennis Juan Ma

Kathy Wyatt

Patrick Boyer

Richard Phipps

Masha Karpushina

Edward Crutchley

Caroline Church

Greg Becker

Shailesh Khandeparkar

James Hamilton Butler

Chris Ede

Stuart Simmons

John Holder

Mark Watkinson

Peter Kyprianou

Martin Hargreaves

Matthew Hollings

Paul Holland

Jonathan Williams

Tianyin Wang

Chris King

Simon Williams

Sara Hingle

Claire Rollet

Kavel Rafferty

Max Gregor

Matthew Laznicka

Dave Curd

Philip Bannister

Derek Bacon

Rachel Oxley

Talya Baldwin

Michael Frith

Peter Thom

Philip Smiley

Rowan Newton

Claire Scully

Stuart Holmes

Echo Chernik

Daniel O'Leary

Ian Murray

Sonia Kretschmar

Vince Ray

Lee Montgomery

Barry Patterson

Chuck Carter

Tom Steyer

Ian Naylor

Jamel Akib

IGNITE

Anne Wilson

CUBE

Bertrand Le Pautremat

Danny Allison

Zoe More O'Ferrall

Alyana Cazalet

Paul Daviz

Kathryn Rathke

Stik

Gail Armstrong

Gray Jolliffe

Bill Greenhead

Keith Robinson

Adam Larkum

Andy Hammond

Britt Spencer

NL Green

Laurence Cleyet-Merle

Natalie Kilany

Xiao Zhou

Bee Willey

Steven Pattison

Victoria Ball

Linda Bronson

Nick Price

Fernando Juarez

TS Spookytooth

Xiao Xin

Frederique Vayssieres

Grahame Baker Smith

Mike Stones

KATMO

Matthew Robson

Vincent Vigla

John Paul Early

James Hodgkins

Willie Ryan

Tim Bradford

Alan Baker

Tobias Jones

Colin Elgie

Nick Diggory

Mark Oliver

Rosie Sanders

Sholto Walker

Petula Stone

Antonia Enthoven

Peter Garland

Andrew Hutchinson

Andrew Beckett

Syd Brak

Roger Kent

Rod & Kira Josey

Steinar Lund

Liz Pepperell

Philip Bishop

Ruth Palmer

www.apple.co.uk

Delivering bespoke illustration
and animation around the world

194

t: +44(0)1724 289081
e: info@apple.co.uk

195

Nathaniel Eckstrom

Mark Sofilas

Pablo Bernasconi

Scott Kennedy

Ned Culic

Steve Graham

The **Overall Picture**

Phone: +61 2 9719 3541
Fax: +61 2 9719 3542
Email: robert@overallpicture.com

www.overallpicture.com

196

Sergio Medina

Daniel Malecki

Donna Cross

Roger Harvey

Jim Tsinganos

David Legge

Formula 1 Car. Christmas poster campaign for Silverstone Race Circuit.

'Fashion'. Supplement for The Daily Telegraph (London).

Matthew Dartford / Flip CG

début **art** • Illustrators, Photographers and Fine Artists Agents
30 Tottenham Street, London, W1T 4RJ. United Kingdom
Tel: 01144 20 7636 1064. Fax: 01144 20 7580 7017
The Coningsby Gallery • Tel: 01144 20 7636 7478

email: **info@debutart.com** • **www.debutart.com**

début **art**

début art • Illustrators, Photographers and Fine Artists Agents
30 Tottenham Street, London, W1T 4RJ. United Kingdom
Tel: 01144 20 7636 1064. Fax: 01144 20 7580 7017
The Coningsby Gallery • Tel: 01144 20 7636 7478
email: **info@debutart.com** • **www.debutart.com**

Since 1985, *début* **art** (based in London, England and now with offices in New York, Amsterdam and Sydney) has proactively sought out leading contemporary image-makers & clients who create original, progressive and commercially successful media material. Today, *début* **art** and the highly artistic illustrators it promotes, are widely regarded, both in the UK and around the world, as representing one of the finest and most contemporary talent groupings in the field of illustration.

début **art** and the illustrators it markets have successfully undertaken assignments worldwide for very many companies that are leaders in their fields including: Microsoft, Apple, Coca-Cola, Proctor and Gamble, Samsung, Levi's, Nokia, Rolls-Royce, BP, Shell, Nike, The Chicago Mercantile Exchange, The NYSE, The London Stock Exchange, Bloomberg, American Express, Barclaycard, HSBC, IBM, British Airways, Unilever, Harrods, Selfridges, Macy's (New York), Topshop, Verizon, Lucas Inc, The Royal Opera House (London), Universal Music, Sony, Miller, Burton, Harper Collins, The Wall Street Journal, The New York Times, The Times (London), Le Monde, The Economist, The Financial Times, Vogue, Cosmopolitan and National Geographic Magazine.

Full portfolios for every artist can be reviewed and requested via our web site at **www.debutart.com**

The Coningsby Gallery stages some 30 exhibitions per year by selected leading illustrators, photographers and fine artists. Review of previous exhibitions, a look at upcoming shows and a photo tour of the gallery itself can be accessed at **www.coningsbygallery.com**

Contact: Andrew Coningsby, Samuel Summerskill, Jonathan Hedley and Rhiannon Lloyd.

Fusako Akimoto	Celyn	The Hejz	Lie-ins & Tigers	Steve Rawlings	Dominic Trevett
David Angel	Container Plus	Matt Herring	Daniel Mackie	Nick Reddyhoff	Alex Trochut
Arno	Matthew Cooper	Oliver Hibert	Harry Malt	Red	Jim Tsinganos
Andrew Baker	Peter Crowther	Nanette Hoogslag	Stephane Manel	Redseal	Vault49
Istvan Banyai	Marta Cerda	Sarah Howell	Sophie Marsham	Craig Robinson	Stephanie Von Reiswitz
Gary Bates	Matthew Dartford	Barbara Hulanicki	Kim McGillivray	Kerry Roper	Jeff Wack
Glen Baxter	Carol del Angel	Ilovedust	Vince McIndoe	Saeko	Craig Ward
Sara Beazley	Barry Downard	Infomen	Justin Metz	Serge Seidlitz	Neil Webb
Jon Berkeley	Rowena Dugdale	Jacey	Pat Morgan	Seripop	Webbo
Pablo Bernasconi	Katie Edwards	Jackdaw	Morten Morland	Craig Shuttlewood	Jane Webster
Raymond Biesinger	Tim Ellis	Paul Jackson	Huntley/Muir	Kid Spaniard	Joe Wilson
Jacquie Boyd	Flatliner	Sarah Jones	Christian Northeast	Bridget Strachan	Oscar Wilson
Norm Breyfogle	Flatliner V2	Viktor Koen	David Newton	Michel Streich	Alex Williamson
Jon Burgerman	Freya	Justin Krietemeyer	Chris Nurse	Tado	Tina Zellmer
Oliver Burston	Peter Grundy	Alan Kitching	Martin O'Neill	James Taylor	Jurgen Ziewe
Benedict Campbell	Sarah Hanson	Ronald Kurniawan	Pietari Posti	The Studio	
James Carey	Richard Hart	Christina K	Paul Price	Yehrin Tong	
Marina Caruso	Hawaii	Neil Leslie	Peter Quinnell	Sophie Toulouse	

'Beauty is truth, truth beauty'
John Keats

Bish: Nights At The Circus Album cover for Gryphon Records.

Comm. by SoBeFit Magazine.

Mermaid. Embroidery design for Maharishi Womenswear.

Comm. for Kirin Beer.

Yehrin Tong

début **art**

Comm. for Carpe Diem.

Comm. by EMI for Alex Cartana album cover.

Comm. for Meteor Global Mobile.

Comm. by Pure Magazine.

Sarah Howell

début **art** • Illustrators, Photographers and Fine Artists Agents
30 Tottenham Street, London, W1T 4RJ. United Kingdom
Tel: 01144 20 7636 1064. Fax: 01144 20 7580 7017
The Coningsby Gallery • Tel: 01144 20 7636 7478

email: **info@debutart.com** • **www.debutart.com**

début **art**

Sara Beazley. Self-initiated.

Matt Herring. Comm. by Healthy Magazine.

Sarah Jones. Self-initiated.

Infomen. Comm. for Levi Strauss.

Flatliner V2. Comm. by Fierce Angels Records.

Carol Del Angel. Self-initiated.

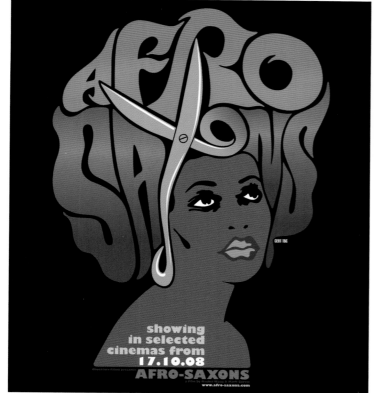

Oscar Wilson. Comm. for Afro-Saxons film poster.

Andrew Baker. Comm. by Forum for the Future.

'Dog Day Afternoon', Self-initiated.

'A is for Acid', Self-initiated.

Ad for Honda (USA). Comm. by RPA.

Vault49

début **art** • Illustrators, Photographers and Fine Artists Agents
30 Tottenham Street, London, W1T 4RJ. United Kingdom
Tel: 01144 20 7636 1064. Fax: 01144 20 7580 7017
The Coningsby Gallery • Tel: 01144 20 7636 7478

email: **info@debutart.com** • **www.debutart.com**

204

début **art**

Self-initiated.

Comm. for Procter & Gamble's 'Ready U' campaign.

Jackdaw

début **art** • Illustrators, Photographers and Fine Artists Agents
30 Tottenham Street, London, W1T 4RJ. United Kingdom
Tel: 01144 20 7636 1064. Fax: 01144 20 7580 7017
The Coningsby Gallery • Tel: 01144 20 7636 7478

email: **info@debutart.com** • **www.debutart.com**

début **art**

205

'Story telling in Contemporay Design'. Comm. by Forum Aid Design Magazine.

'Seattle'. Comm. by WBY Magazine.

Comm. by Story Worldwide for IATA's Airline Magazine 'Air Cargo'.

'Specialist Due Diligence'. Comm. by Real Deals Magazine.

Neil Webb

début **art** • Illustrators, Photographers and Fine Artists Agents
30 Tottenham Street, London, W1T 4RJ. United Kingdom
Tel: 01144 20 7636 1064. Fax: 01144 20 7580 7017
The Coningsby Gallery • Tel: 01144 20 7636 7478

email: **info@debutart.com** • **www.debutart.com**

début **art**

Comm. for Vodafone.

Comm. by The Science Museum (UK).

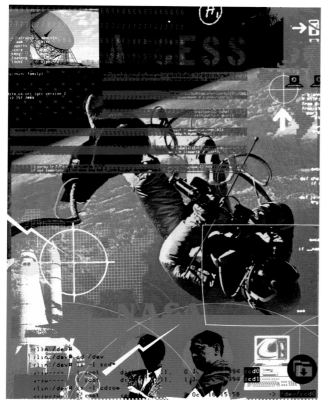

'Hacking into NASA'. Comm. by Business Week Magazine.

Comm. by Fortune Magazine.

Alex Williamson

début **art** • Illustrators, Photographers and Fine Artists Agents
30 Tottenham Street, London, W1T 4RJ. United Kingdom
Tel: 01144 20 7636 1064. Fax: 01144 20 7580 7017
The Coningsby Gallery • Tel: 01144 20 7636 7478

email: **info@debutart.com** • **www.debutart.com**

début **art**

Comm. by Partners Andrew Aldridge for Vodafone.

Nike Air Jordan.

Coldplay. Comm. by GQ Magazine.

Poster ad for NFL Tennessee Titans (USA). Comm. by Reebok.

Patrick Morgan

début **art** • Illustrators, Photographers and Fine Artists Agents
30 Tottenham Street, London, W1T 4RJ. United Kingdom
Tel: 01144 20 7636 1064. Fax: 01144 20 7580 7017
The Coningsby Gallery • Tel: 01144 20 7636 7478

email: **info@debutart.com** • **www.debutart.com**

Comm. by Money 100 Magazine.

Comm. for Vodafone.

Comm. by Liberty's Store (UK) for an Autumn-Winter Fashion Book.

James Taylor

début **art** • Illustrators, Photographers and Fine Artists Agents
30 Tottenham Street, London, W1T 4RJ. United Kingdom
Tel: 01144 20 7636 1064. Fax: 01144 20 7580 7017
The Coningsby Gallery • Tel: 01144 20 7636 7478

email: **info@debutart.com** • **www.debutart.com**

début **art**

Paul McCartney. Comm. by Snob Magazine.

Dark Knight. Comm. by GQ Magazine (UK).

Portland Street scene. Self-initiated.

Ex Chief Executive of BP. Lord Browne. Comm. by BP Magazine.

James Carey

début **art** • Illustrators, Photographers and Fine Artists Agents
30 Tottenham Street, London, W1T 4RJ. United Kingdom
Tel: 01144 20 7636 1064. Fax: 01144 20 7580 7017
The Coningsby Gallery • Tel: 01144 20 7636 7478

email: **info@debutart.com** • **www.debutart.com**

début **art**

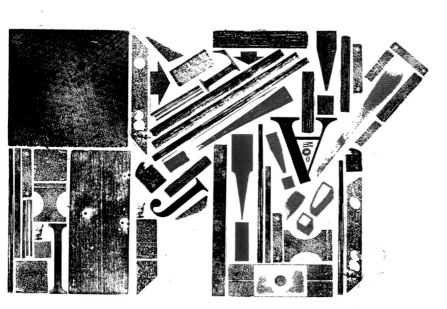

Comm. by MTV.

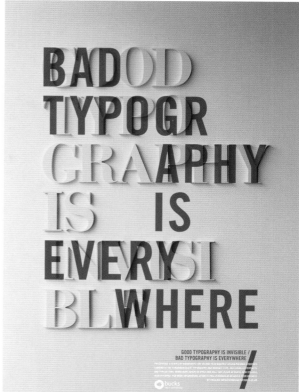

Comm. by Buckinghamshire Chiltern's University.

Self-initiated.

'The World on a Plate'. Comm. for The Economist.

Craig Ward

début **art** • Illustrators, Photographers and Fine Artists Agents
30 Tottenham Street, London, W1T 4RJ. United Kingdom
Tel: 01144 20 7636 1064. Fax: 01144 20 7580 7017
The Coningsby Gallery • Tel: 01144 20 7636 7478

email: **info@debutart.com** • **www.debutart.com**

début **art**

'Your Amazing Brain'. Comm. by Dorling Kindersley.

Comm. for Robinsons Fruitshoot.

'Number Association'. Comm. by Dorling Kindersley.

Serge Seidlitz

début **art** • Illustrators, Photographers and Fine Artists Agents
30 Tottenham Street, London, W1T 4RJ. United Kingdom
Tel: 01144 20 7636 1064. Fax: 01144 20 7580 7017
The Coningsby Gallery • Tel: 01144 20 7636 7478

email: **info@debutart.com** • **www.debutart.com**

'A Trip Down the Amazon'. Comm. by The Times (London).

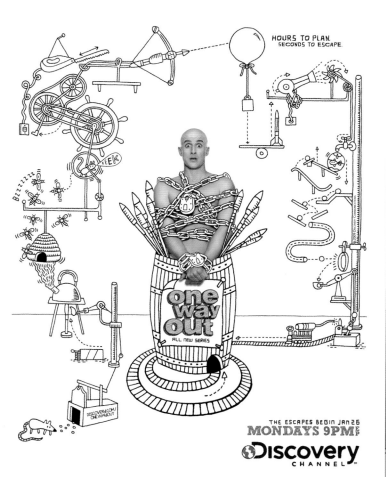

'Jonathan Goodwin's One Way Out'. Comm. by The Discovery Channel.

Comm. for Garden Burger.

Morten Morland. Comm. by The Times (London).

Jane Webster. Comm. for 1792 Ridgemont Reserve.

Gary Bates. Comm. by Women's Weekly Magazine.

Craig Shuttlewood. Comm. for NU Vision.

Peter Grundy. Comm. by Shell.

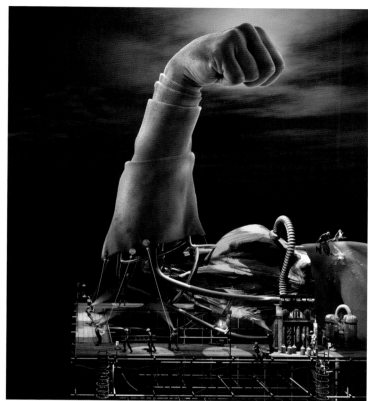

Barry Downard. Comm. by Men's Health Magazine.

Pietari Posti. Comm. by USA Today.

Jurgen Ziewe. Comm. by Schroders.

début **art**

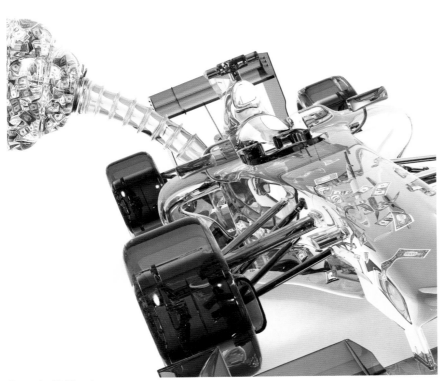

Comm. by F1 Magazine.

Comm. by Siemens Magazine.

Comm. by SoBeFit Magazine.

Comm. by Worth Magazine (USA).

Peter Crowther

début **art** • Illustrators, Photographers and Fine Artists Agents
30 Tottenham Street, London, W1T 4RJ. United Kingdom
Tel: 01144 20 7636 1064. Fax: 01144 20 7580 7017
The Coningsby Gallery • Tel: 01144 20 7636 7478

email: **info@debutart.com** • **www.debutart.com**

Comm. by T3 Magazine.

Comm. by People Management Magazine.

Comm. by F1 Magazine.

Comm. by The Guardian Guide.

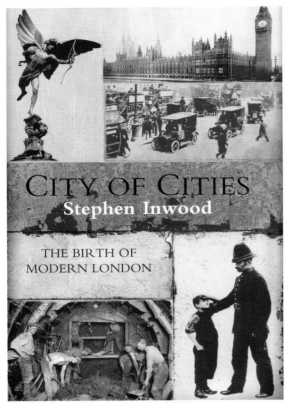

Kim McGillivray. Comm. by Macmillan Publishing.

Kerry Roper. Self-initiated.

Dominic Trevett. Comm. by Penguin Books.

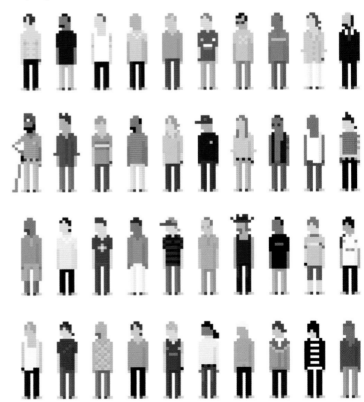

Craig Robinson. Comm. for Reebok.

début **art** • Illustrators, Photographers and Fine Artists Agents
30 Tottenham Street, London, W1T 4RJ. United Kingdom
Tel: 01144 20 7636 1064. Fax: 01144 20 7580 7017
The Coningsby Gallery • Tel: 01144 20 7636 7478

email: **info@debutart.com** • **www.debutart.com**

début **art**

Self-initiated.

Self-initiated.

'Irrestible Offers'. Comm. by O2.

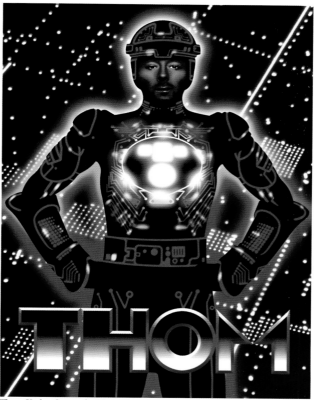

Thom Yorke. Comm. by Mojo Magazine.

Arno

début **art** • Illustrators, Photographers and Fine Artists Agents
30 Tottenham Street, London, W1T 4RJ. United Kingdom
Tel: 01144 20 7636 1064. Fax: 01144 20 7580 7017
The Coningsby Gallery • Tel: 01144 20 7636 7478

email: **info@debutart.com** • **www.debutart.com**

début **art**

219

Comm. by Wired Magazine.

Comm. by Foreign Direct Investment Magazine for renewable energy feature.

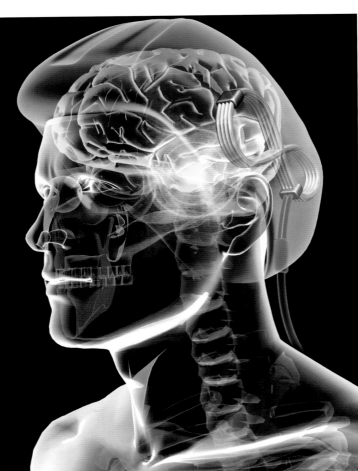

Comm. by BBC FOCUS Magazine.

Oliver Burston

début **art** • Illustrators, Photographers and Fine Artists Agents
30 Tottenham Street, London, W1T 4RJ. United Kingdom
Tel: 01144 20 7636 1064. Fax: 01144 20 7580 7017
The Coningsby Gallery • Tel: 01144 20 7636 7478

email: **info@debutart.com** • **www.debutart.com**

début **art**

'Digital Kids' for Healthy Kids (USA).

Comm. by British Airways Magazine.

'Predictions' for IKEA Room Magazine.

Comm. for Walkers Crisps.

David Newton

début **art** • Illustrators, Photographers and Fine Artists Agents
30 Tottenham Street, London, W1T 4RJ. United Kingdom
Tel: 01144 20 7636 1064. Fax: 01144 20 7580 7017
The Coningsby Gallery • Tel: 01144 20 7636 7478

email: **info@debutart.com** • **www.debutart.com**

début **art**

221

'Diving Into The Data'. Comm. by Ode Magazine.

'SOS Supply Chain'. Comm. by Business Voice.

'Work Relocations'. Comm. by Design Week.

'ebooks'. Comm. by Condé Nast Traveler.

Neil Webb

début **art** • Illustrators, Photographers and Fine Artists Agents
30 Tottenham Street, London, W1T 4RJ. United Kingdom
Tel: 01144 20 7636 1064. Fax: 01144 20 7580 7017
The Coningsby Gallery • Tel: 01144 20 7636 7478

email: **info@debutart.com** • **www.debutart.com**

début **art**

The Steady Investor, *T. Rowe Price*

A Very Little Princess, *Random House*

elizabeth sayles

...a hint of otherworldliness...

845.267.4127

liz@elizabethsayles.com

www.elizabethsayles.com

directoryofillustration.com/elizabethsayles

represented in the children's market by Cornell & McCarthy, LLC / www.cmartreps.com / 203.454.4210

Parker Fulton 410-360-5981 cciART.com

Michael Meister
represented by
Wanda Nowak artists' representative
www.wandanow.com www.michaelmeister.com

THINGS HAVE CHANGED

Bernard **Adnet**   Shirley **Beckes**   Pamela **Carroll**   Nelle **Davis**   Daniel **Delvalle**   Pat & Robin **DeWitt**   Shelley **Dieterichs**
Mordicai **Gerstein**   Mike **Gordon**   Gershom **Griffith**   Christine **Jenny**   Jan **Naimo Jones**   Sophie **Kittredge**   Loretta **Krupinski**
Vickie **Learner**   Joe **LeMonnier**   Mike **Maydak**   Kay **McCabe**   Tim **Pfeiffer**   Miriam **Sagasti**   Heather **Solomon**   Tom **Sperling**   N Jo **Tufts**

Kolea Baker *Artists Representative*
206-784-1136   kolea@kolea.com   www.kolea.com

Kolea Baker *Artists Representative*
206-784-1136 kolea@kolea.com www.kolea.com

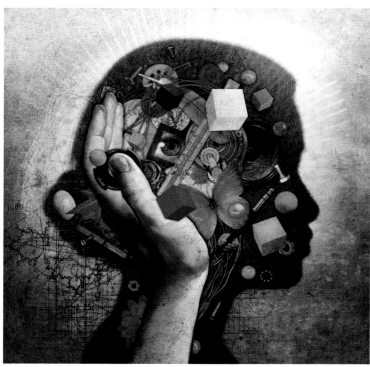

Kolea Baker Artists Representative
206-784-1136 kolea@kolea.com www.kolea.com

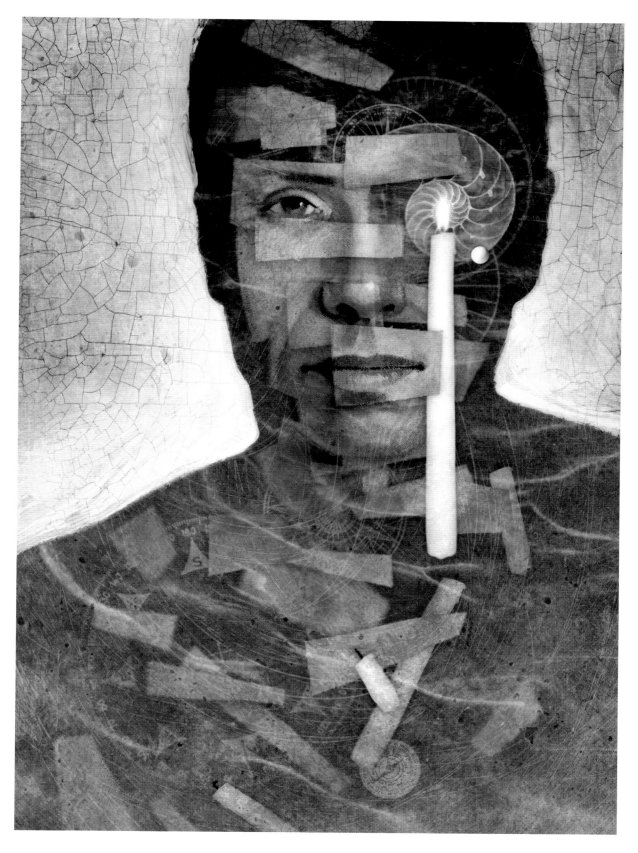

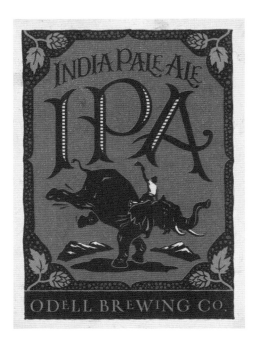

Kolea Baker *Artists Representative*
206-784-1136   kolea@kolea.com   www.kolea.com

Kolea Baker *Artists Representative*
206-784-1136 kolea@kolea.com www.kolea.com

Kolea Baker Artists Representative
206-784-1136 kolea@kolea.com www.kolea.com

Kolea Baker *Artists Representative*
206-784-1136   kolea@kolea.com   www.kolea.com

Kolea Baker Artists Representative
206-784-1136 kolea@kolea.com www.kolea.com

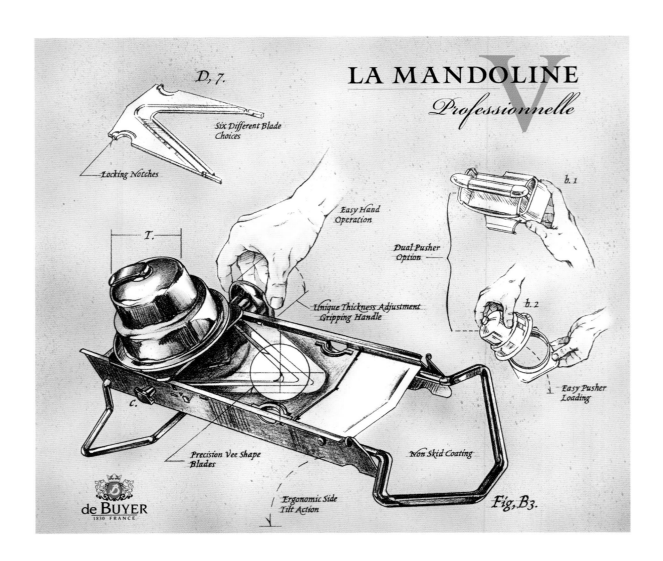

D, 7.

Six Different Blade Choices

Locking Notches

LA MANDOLINE
V
Professionnelle

Easy Hand Operation

b. 1

Dual Pusher Option

I.

Unique Thickness Adjustment Gripping Handle

b. 2

Easy Pusher Loading

C.

Precision Vee Shape Blades

Non Skid Coating

Ergonomic Side Tilt Action

Fig, B3.

de BUYER
1830 FRANCE

CHARDONNAY

Chalk Hill Estate
North Founders Block
Clone 95
Dijon, France

Nature's Gate
ORGANICS™

certified organic ingredients

soy milk
fragrance-free
for sensitive skin

CREAMY SHAVE GEL

Nature's Gate
ORGANICS™

certified organic ingredients

cucumber & mint
ultra moisturizing

SHOWER & BATH GEL

Kolea Baker *Artists Representative*
206-784-1136 kolea@kolea.com www.kolea.com

Russ Charpentier

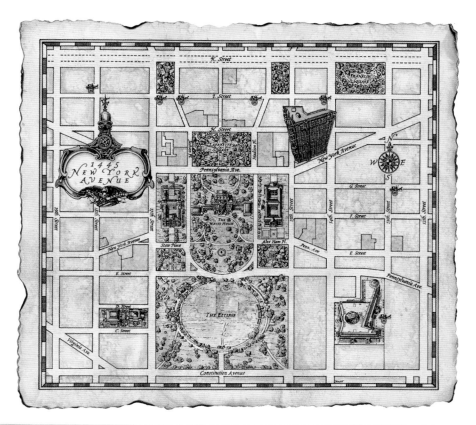

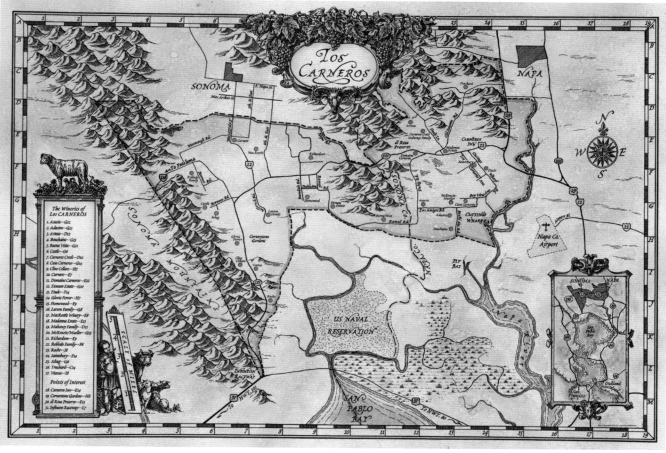

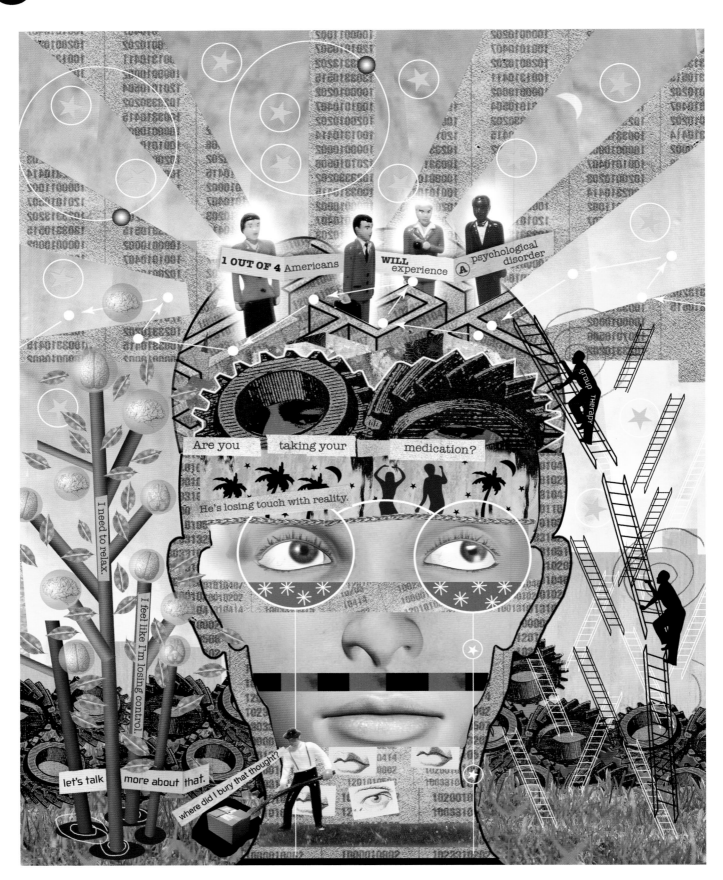

Kolea Baker *Artists Representative*
206-784-1136 kolea@kolea.com www.kolea.com

Kolea Baker *Artists Representative*
206-784-1136 kolea@kolea.com www.kolea.com

Kolea Baker Artists Representative
206-784-1136 kolea@kolea.com www.kolea.com

Bjorn Thorkelson

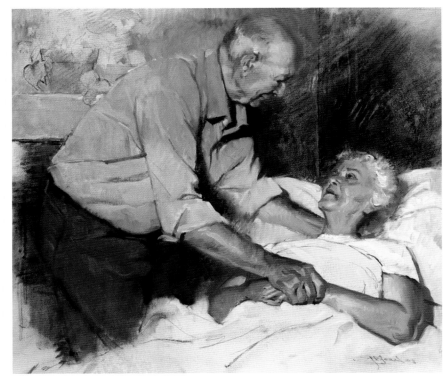

Kolea Baker *Artists Representative*
206-784-1136 kolea@kolea.com www.kolea.com

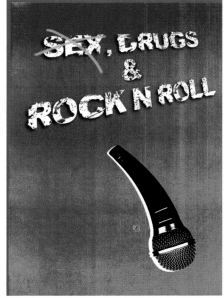

249

AMY NING

SUDI McCOLLUM

LIZ SANDERS AGENCY

TELEPHONE: (509) 993-6400   *there's more at* LIZSANDERS.COM   FACSIMILE: (509) 466-5400

LIZ SANDERS AGENCY

TELEPHONE: (509) 993-6400   *there's more at* LIZSANDERS.com   FACSIMILE: (509) 466-5400

JARED BECKSTRAND

County Studio
International Ltd

Paper engineering and illustration by Brian Bartle, Neil Capel,

Tel: +44 (0)1530 222 260   Fax: +44 (0)1530 222 127

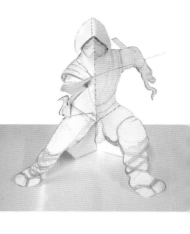

Gemma Denham, Stuart Martin, Dudley Moseley and Sylvia Ward.

Inspired by excellence

email: dud@countystudio.com   www.countystudio.com

I-Hua Chen ILLUSTRATION & DESIGN

REPRESENTED BY Francisco Delgadillo, GESTUDIA

415.601.3355 | principal@gestudia.com

COMMISSIONED CONCEPT FOR BOOK PROPOSAL

COMMISSIONED BY ORACLE MAGAZINE FOR A RETAIL ARTICLE

COMM. BY SIEBEL CUSTOMER WORLD MAGAZINE FOR GOVERNMENT SERVICES

ihuadesign.com

THE ILLUSTRATION CORPORATION ®

Susan Hatten (ARTIST'S REP) · susan@illustrationcorporation.com · 816.820.7262 · WWW.ILLUSTRATIONCORPORATION.COM

Nº 7 name: employee: SAM SPRATLIN
code: comments: ID 504338

Nº 2 name: employee: ALLIE ARMSTRONG
code: comments: ID 837462

Nº 3 name: employee: JESSE HORA
code: comments: ID 024456

ESTD 2008

Nº 9 name: employee: ALEX FULLER
code: comments: ID 504338

Nº 4 name: employee: GABE USADEL
code: comments:

Nº 1 name: employee: ERIC ELLIS
code: comments: ID 024456

ORDER NUMBER:

JOHN SOLOMINE

Oh, HEY! Gosh my new neighbor is so loud. I swear he must weigh 2000 pounds!!!

CETATE GRAPHIC ART AIDS

Nº 8 name: employee: CHAD KOURI
code: comments: ID 837462

☑ deer ☑ giraffe ☑ bear ☑ goose

Nº 5 name: employee: ROD HUNTING
code: comments: ID 024456

PRINTED IN U.S.A

property of illustration corporation

STANLEY MOUSE

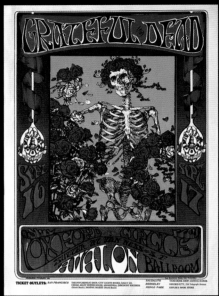

AVALON BALLROOM 1966

LIFE MAGAZINE 1967

mousestudios.com/v
CONTACT: ANMARIE LINSLEY
801 453 0300
publicimage@aol.com

ALTOIDS

MOTORIZR

MOTOROLA / ROLLINGSTONE MAGAZINE

CONVERSE

"THE MAN WHO DREW THE FACE ON ROCK MUSIC"
JOE SELVIN

THESE POSTERS ARE WORKS OF LOVE
_MICK JAGGER

MOUSEART MAKES MY HEART SAY, "CHEESE"
HOWARD HESSMAN

MUSEUM SHOWS:
THE SMITHSONIAN INSTITUTE.
THE NEW YORK MUSEUM OF MODERN ART.
HE BOSTON MUSEUM.
THE ART MUSEUM OF SAN FRANCISCO.
SAN DIEGO MUSEUM.
UNIVERSITY OF SANTA BARBARA ART MUSEUM.
SAN FRANCISCO MOMA.
THE OAKLAND MUSEUM THE HERMATAGE.

DOORS CD COVER 2008

ANITA GRIEN
155 East 38th Street
New York, NY 10016
Tel (212) 697-6170
Fax (212) 697-6177
www.anitagrien.com
anita@anitagrien.com

Representing:
Ron Carboni
Higgins Bond
Julie Johnson
Anthony Jenkins
Alan Neider
Alan Reingold

Also Representing:
Fanny Mellet Berry
Bruce Cayard

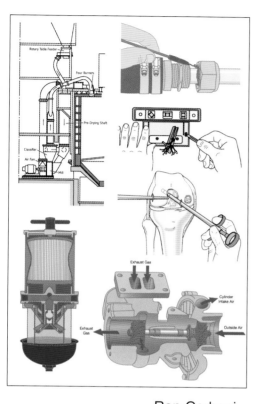

Ron Carboni

Higgins Bond

Julie Johnson

Anthony Jenkins

Alan Neider

Alan Reingold

"The Fall of Man"

SHAOLINFURY.COM

DUNG HOANG IS REPRESENTED BY FURIOUS VISUAL WORLD

CLIENTS INCLUDE CONVERSE, ELEKTRA RECORDS, DREAMWORKS, PLAYBOY, GQ, BEST LIFE, ESQUIRE, INC., THE ATLANTIC MONTHLY, AND THE NEW YORK TIMES

Kelly Pierce

Jeff Pollard / icons / logos

Kym Foster

Bruce Hutchison

Jason Lynch

TRUE

Christer Eriksson

Colin Poole

Wayne Watford

Tom Ward

Paul Borchers

Sue Rother

Juan Alvarez

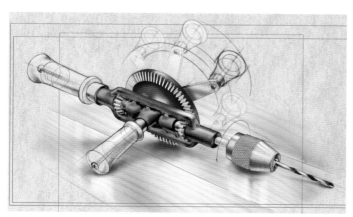

John Francis

Bill Lesniewski

Bob Berry

ILLUSTRATION & DESIGN INC.

www.bobberryillustration.com

38 Deer View Lane,
Poughquag, New York 12570

Telephone and Fax: 845-223-7925

E-Mail: berryart@frontiernet.net

See Additional samples @:
www.directoryofillustration.com go to index/ Bob Berry

Little Dev and Scba Kids by Simon Cranston

Super Why and Wonder Red by Bob Berry

Thomas the Tank Engine by Bob Berry

Frahm Downtown and
Stand Alone ©
2009 by Gio

Representing the illustrations of:
Bob Berry, Character Design and Licensed Characters
Rom Valker, Fantasy and Sci-Fi Illustration

Simon Cranston, Fun and Zany Characters
The Mighty Quinn, Retro Cartoons and Anime
Giovani Diaz, Urban Themes and Manga

Deadeye Digger Jones by Rom Valker

ice Ranger by
Rom Valker

Free Realms by Rom Valker

Amelia Starheart by Bob Berry

Free Realm Troll by Rom Valker

Tyson from " Beyblades"
byThe Mighty Quinn

Space Ghost by
The Mighty Quinn

Sean Farrell

SEAN FARRELL

Shelton Leong

ILLUSTRATION

Deborah Melmon

SHELTON LEONG

DEBORAH MELMON

represented by **Sharon Morris** associates 415•987•4517

see more images at: www.sharonartrep.com

Partini

A party game for the laugh-out-loud crowd!

For Adults
Individual or Team Play

JASON**MUNGER** JASONMUNGER.COM 902-889-2505 JASON@JASONMUNGER.COM
REPRESENTED BY REACTOR ART & DESIGN REACTOR.CA 416-703-1913 HELLO@REACTOR.CA

ROGER ROTH   DIANE TESKE HARRIS   P. DVORAK   PIP THEO   GEOFFREY MOSS

MARION MOSKOWITZ REPRESENTS INC

212.517.4919 www.moskyreps.com 315 east 68th st. new york city 10021

b.szost@portfoliosolutionsllc.com
136 JAMESON HILL ROAD, CLINTON CORNERS, NY 12514
845-266-1001
www.portfoliosolutionsllc.com

PORTFOLIO **S**OLUTIONS

Representing the finest illustrators available to work in all markets requiring artwork for children.

Bernadette Szost - Artists' Representative   b.szost@portfoliosolutionsllc.com

Jane Yamada | Liza Woodruff | Jenny Williams | Teri Weidner | Lucia G. Washburn | Rebecca Thornburgh | Kaori Tajima

Robert Squier | Elena Selivanova | Carol Schwartz | Ronnie Rooney | Dana Regan | Marcy Ramsey | Beatriz Helena Ramos

Cary Pillo | Stephen Marchesi | Sharon Lane Holm | Kathie Kelleher | Pamela Johnson | Amy Huntington

www.portfoliosolutionsllc.com

Patrick Girouard | Mernie Gallagher-Cole | Laura Freeman | Laura Ferraro Close

Len Epstein | Creston Ely | Jeffrey Ebbeler | Ryan Durney | Brian Caleb Dumm | Michelle Dorenkamp | Bert Dodson

Susan DeSantis | Ted Dawson | Jane Conteh-Morgan | Eulala Conner | Roberta Collier-Morales | Derrick Chow | Jean Cassels

  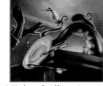 

Paige Billin-Frye | Dawn Beacon | Winifred Barnum-Newman | Lynne Avril | Michael Allen Austin | R.W. Alley | JoAnn Adinolfi

136 Jameson Hill Road • Clinton Corners • NY • 12514 • 845.266.1001

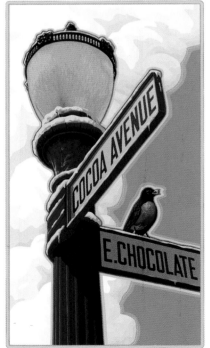

Cabela's

Cabela's

christine prapas

Patrice Barton

Christine Kornacki

Melissa Iwai

John Kanzler

Christina A. Tugeau

(757) 221-0666
www.catugeau.com

Christy Hale

Jeremy Tugeau

Ann Iosa

Julie Downing

Stacey Schuett

Christina A. Tugeau

(757) 221-0666
www.catugeau.com

Johanna Westerman

Damian Ward

Scott R. Brooks

Brent Campbell

Audrey Durney

Chris Lyles

Robbie Short

Kathy Weller

Don Tate

Sehee Jung

Gina Capaldi

Chris Vallo

Dani Jones

C.A. Nobens
Illustration & Design, Inc.

© 2009 C.A. Nobens

• Whimsical
• Educational
• Christian
• Line Art

• Cheryl Nobens •
• Represented by Tugeau2 Artist Representatives •
• 216-707-0854 • www.tugeau2.com •

Thodoris Tibilis
www.tibilis.com
info@tibilis.com

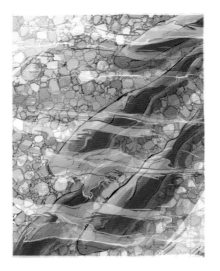

donna pidlubny   623.565.9918   www.donnapidlubny.com
illustration@donnapidlubny.com

Daniel Abramovich

www.abramobastik.com   daniel@abramobastik.com   347.417.3496

Cioppino!

Prawns Tomato Halibut Mussels Basil Garlic Onion Lemon

Blot Line

maryrossillustration.com 415 661-2930

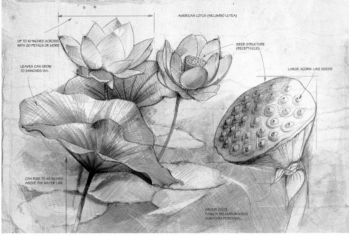

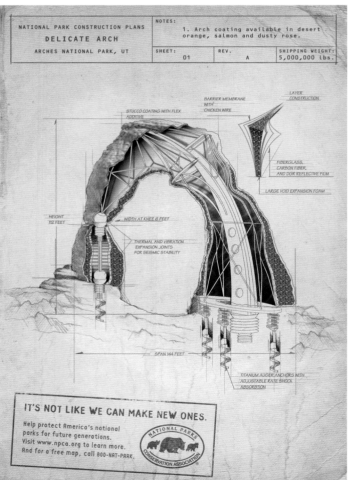

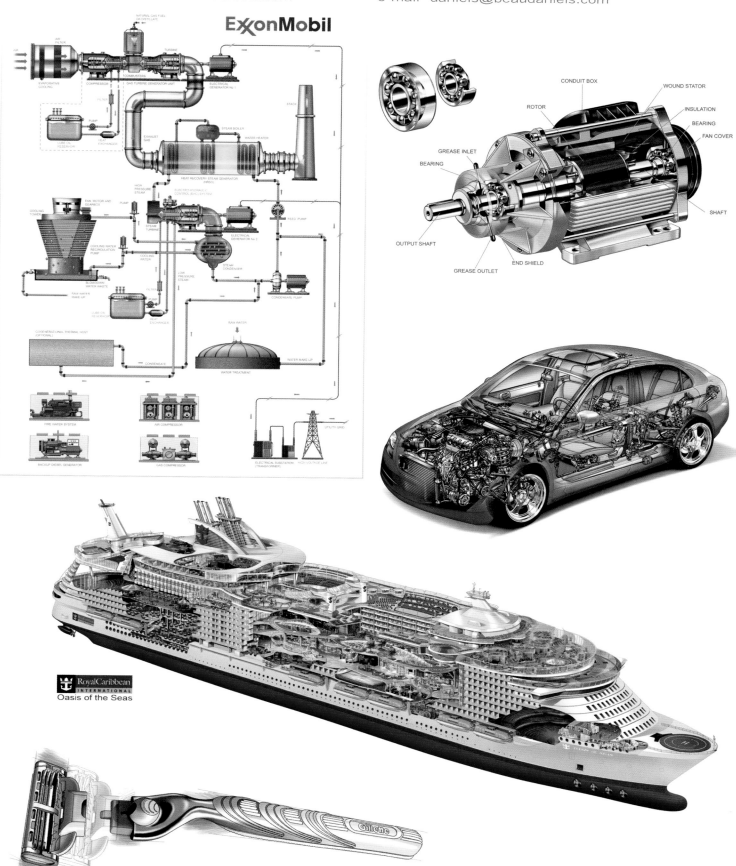

ExxonMobil

RoyalCaribbean
INTERNATIONAL
Oasis of the Seas

Paul Sharp

Sharp Designs & Illustration Inc.
Characters, Package Design, Logos

www.paulsharp.com
studio@paulsharp.com

©Gamewright

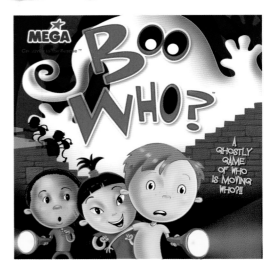

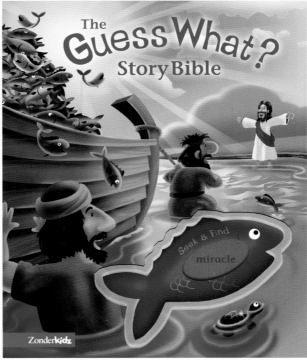

•Oppenheim Toy Portfolio Gold Award •iParenting Media Award •Creative Child Magazine Preferred Choice Award •ECPA Gold Medallion Book Award Finalist

© Paul Sharp

email: psiu88@yahoo.com
www.petersiu.com

Peter SiU

studio 650.692.1839
cell 650.455.4689

ILLUSTRATION PRO

Illustration • Graphic Design • Web Development   847-705-5761   mitchromanowski@sbcglobal.net

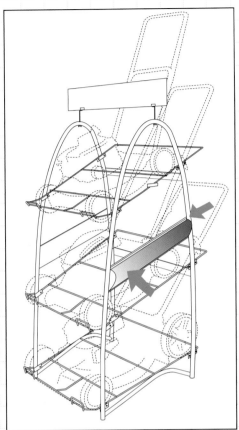

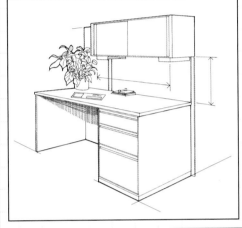

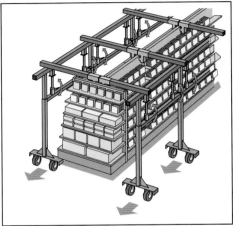

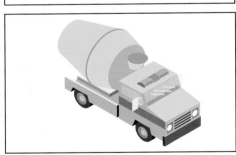

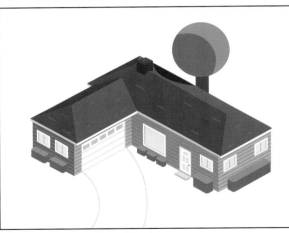

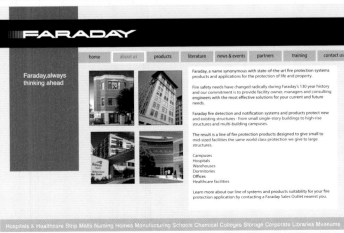

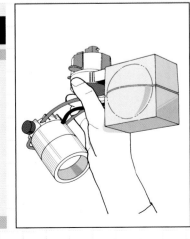

ACME PIXEL®.com

Advertising   **B2B**   **Book**   **Editorial**   **High-Tech**   **VideoGame**

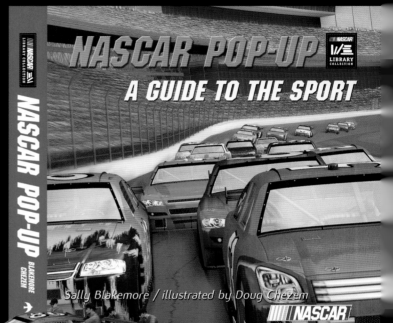

NASCAR LIBRARY COLLECTION

NASCAR POP-UP
A GUIDE TO THE SPORT

NASCAR POP-UP — BLAKEMORE / CHEZEM

Sally Blakemore / illustrated by Doug Chezem

//// **NASCAR**

STURGIS 50 MILES

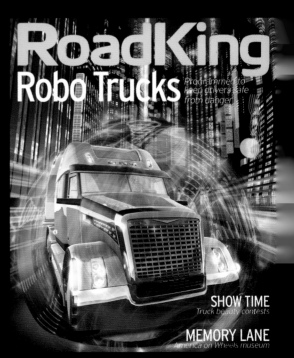

RoadKing
Robo Trucks
Programmed to keep drivers safe from danger

SHOW TIME
Truck beauty contests

MEMORY LANE
America on Wheels museum

Acme Pixel: Digital Illustration and Production Art since 1987

Featuring 3D CG Illustration by **Doug Chezem** Studio:703-591-5424 Office:202-719-0314 infodi@acmepixel.com

Top Dog Studio

26621
NORMANDY RD.
BAY VILLAGE, OH 44140
440.655.7280

KBROWN@TOPDOGSTUDIO.NET
WWW.TOPDOGSTUDIO.ORG

Michael Pallozzi
Design & Illustration
208 West 29th St., Suite 613A
New York, NY 10001

mike@pallozzidigital.com
office 212-290-0312
cell 973-769-3743

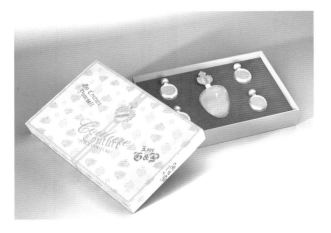

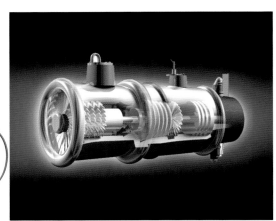

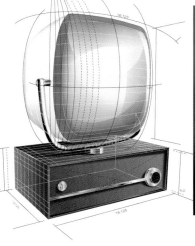

Steve Björkman

949·349·0109   stevebjorkman.com

aaronmeshon.com

Aaron Meshon

(718) 858-8485

SCOTT SEIBEL
ARTIST / ILLUSTRATOR
SCOTT@SEIBELSTUDIO.COM

SEIBELSTUDIO.COM   602-697-4486

MIRA NAMETH

miranameth.com // 646.236.7241 // hello@miranameth.com

the Coke side of life

the Coke side of life

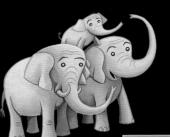

www.brianjones.com

626 356 0061 h

831 566 3642 c

email: briantjones@sbcglobal.net

So quickly Quack hid in a cave
But there, he'd made an error.
A furry shape
Blocked his escape.
"I'm trapped!" he screeched in terror.

In the darkest corner of the zoo
There stood a gloomy shack.

A nearby scrawl read:.

KEEP OUT
ALL !!

JUST LEAVE ME
BE!
signed QUACK

LAURA S BAILEY

WWW.LAURASBAILEY.COM creative problem solving through painterly illustration
laura@laurasbailey.com phone 314|623|5624

Colin Hayes
illustrator, inc

425.338.5452   colin.hayes@verizon.net   www.theispot/artist/chayes

LANCE LEKANDER
WWW.LANCELEKANDER.COM
907.272.0495

icons

ILLUSTRATIONS BY JASON MAMONE
www.jasonmamone.com

GREG NEWBOLD

801 274 2407

GREGNEWBOLD.COM

Malane Newman

(760) 789-4583
www.MalaneNewman.com
malane@malanenewman.com

On A Train

In The Garden

On An Airplane

In The Dining Room

CHILDREN'S PRODUCTS   CHARACTER DESIGN   ILLUSTRATION   WEBSITES   AND MORE!

Chai Masala
black tea whole cardamon
ground stars anise
Bay 2 Paves
crushed black peppercorns
Cloves
HOT MILK
Honey

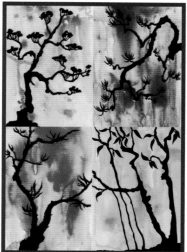

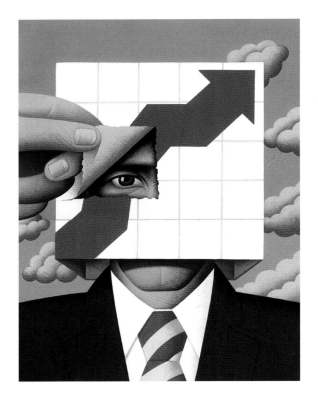

ADAM NIKLEWICZ

203.230.1024   www.illustratorUSA.com

STEPHEN BAILEY

Stephen@sbaileyillustration.com   716·745·3341   www.sbaileyillustration.com

311

JUSTIN WINSLOW
ILLUSTRATION / ANIMATION
917.558.6895 / www.justinwinslow.com / justinnw@gmail.com

JOHN MACDONALD

t: 413~458-0056 • c: 413-884-2074

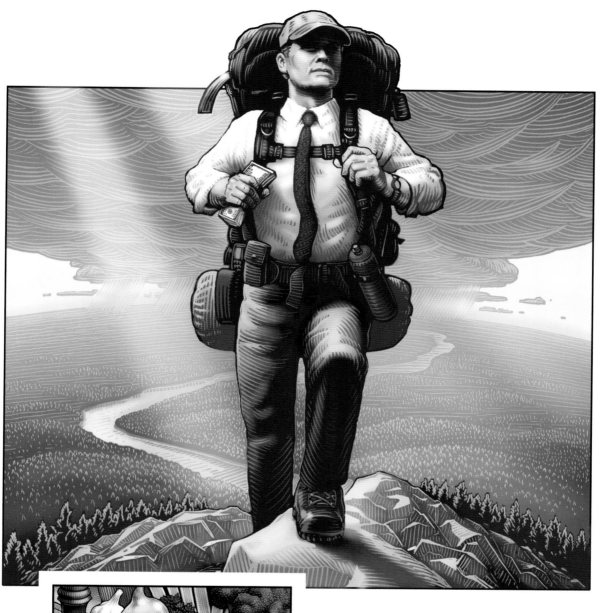

john@jmacdonald.com • www.jmacdonald.com

ruland

michaelruland.com　　t. 281.501.2048

Lael Henderson
801 377 3304
www.laelhenderson.com

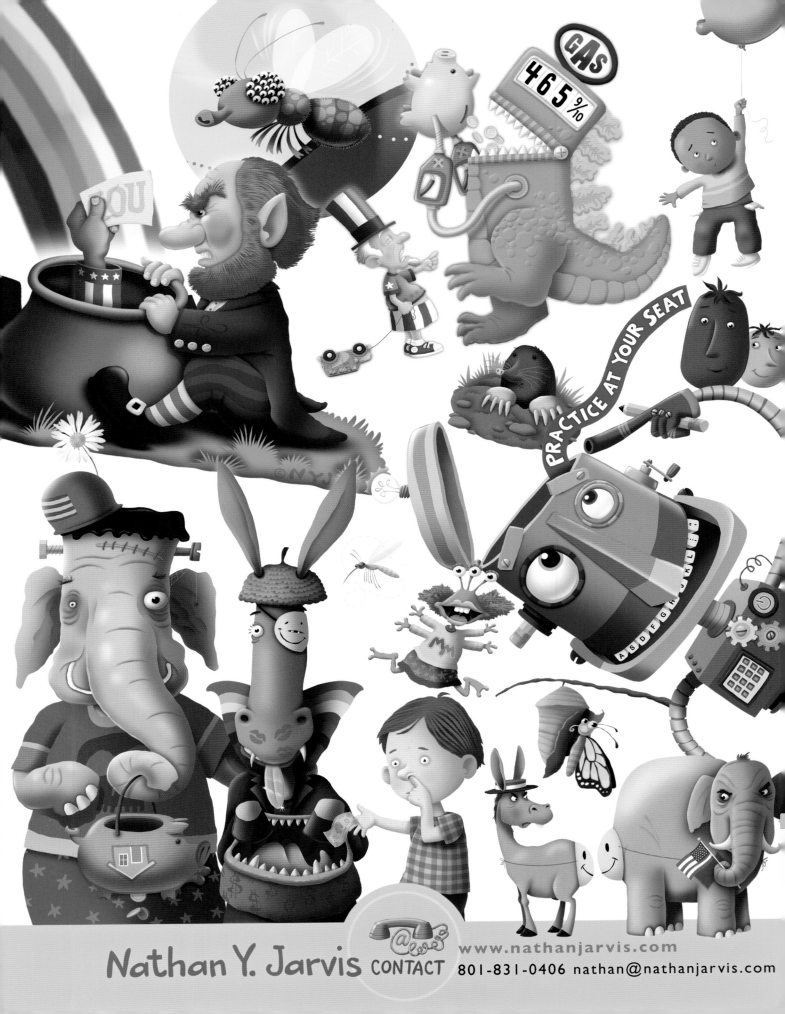

Maria Rabinky

www.rabinkyart.com
maria@rabinkyart.com
877-277-1768

San Francisco

amy hevron

hoo hoo.

(206) 427 9234
amyhevron@gmail.com

novarhyme.com

9 Surf Studios

Tom White

HEALTHCARE ILLUSTRATION

LOGOS & MAGAZINE COVERS

PROMOTION & POS DISPLAY

AWARD WINNING BOOK COVERS

TYPEFACE & WORDMARK DESIGN

212.866.8778
www.9surf.com
9surfstudios.blogspot.com
tom@9surf.com

CONCEPT ILLUSTRATION

COMPLETE PORTFOLIO ONLINE

www.pixel-artist.com
cheri@pixel-artist.com

Cheri Freund

oh la la
kyrakendall.com

Nice work!
nedharrison.com

Pearson

GSWA

Design News

Michelle Barbera
tel: 877.787.9896

www.barberaillustration.com
michelle@barberaillustration.com

Merlin Technologies/ Illusionator

Good Ferret Greetings

Nashville Scene

Silas Meredith
and the New World Salsa Orchestra

Illusionator

Caeco/Gamewright

Dusty Deyo Illustration

web: www.dustydeyo.com
email: dustydeyo@ca.rr.com

phone: (310) 398-2699
fax: (310) 390-7588

Wind Power

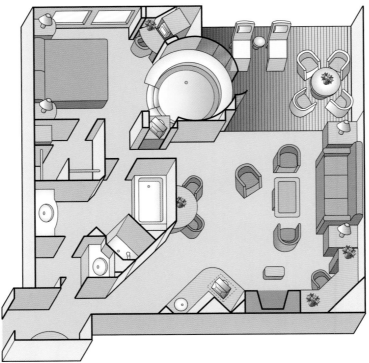

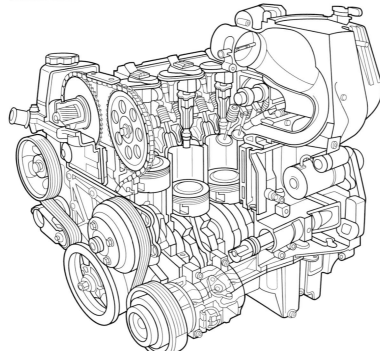

Taia Morley
651.436.8855
taiamorley.com

SIMEON ELSON

WWW.SIMEONELSON.CO.UK | +44 (0)785 539 6215 | INFO@SIMEONELSON.CO.UK

Callie Butler Goodrich

hello beet, crimson treat, garden seat,
grande to petite, obliged to meet,
turn up the heat, bon appetit!

hello

hello@calliegoodrich.com

512 698 0717 or 011 33 6 32 90 59 01

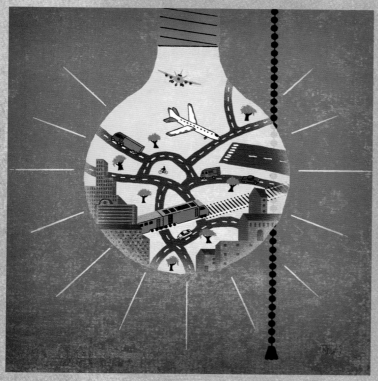

ken orvidas
425.867.3072
orvidas.com

Illustration & Design

by Janet Allinger

allingerj@gmail.com
www.janetallinger.com

831.325.9567

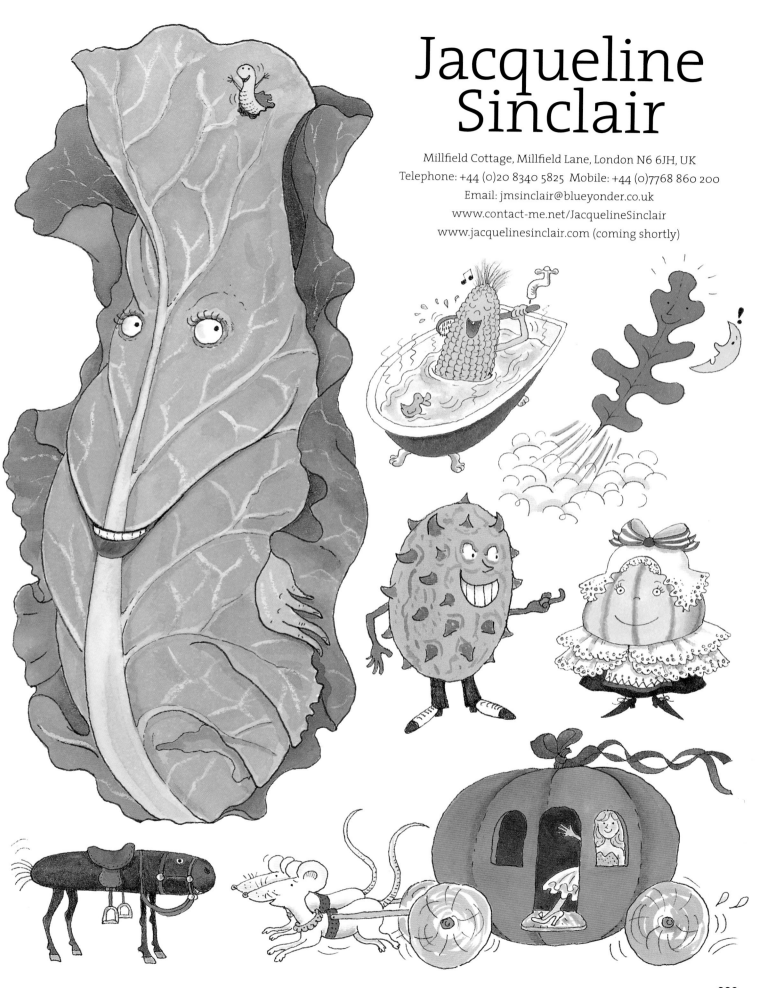

Jacqueline Sinclair

Millfield Cottage, Millfield Lane, London N6 6JH, UK
Telephone: +44 (0)20 8340 5825 Mobile: +44 (0)7768 860 200
Email: jmsinclair@blueyonder.co.uk
www.contact-me.net/JacquelineSinclair
www.jacquelinesinclair.com (coming shortly)

Wesley Bedrosian | Illustration | 100 Montclair Ave | Montclair, NJ 07042 | 973.233.0093 | mail@wesleybedrosian.com

Clients include: The New York Times, Barron's, Vanity Fair, Business Week, Billboard Magazine, Fortune, The Wall Street Journal, The Progressive, Time, Harvard Medical, Forbes, The Boston Globe, The Washington Post, New York Magazine, SmartMoney, The Nation.

dave wheeler studio LLC

www.davewheeler.com | dave@davewheeler.com | 888-454-0800

DOUGLAS SCHNEIDER

231-276-9770
www.douglasschneider.com

Driscoll's Berries

King Orchards

Castella Imports

Tribe Hummus

Dean Foods

Tribe Hummus

La Yogurt

338

SCIENCE-ART.COM

ROGER ANDREWS
ILLUSTRATION

RAND247@AOL.COM   978.896.6166   WWW.RAND247.COM

© Copyright 2009 Ludwig Van Beethoven

AMERICAN EXPRESS

© Copyright 2009 American Express

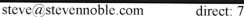
© Copyright 2009 Advanced Micro Devices

© Copyright 2009 Fentiman's

© Copyright 2009 Kennebunport Lobster Company

© Copyright 2009 Boston Beer Company

© Copyright 2009 Publix Supermarkets

© Copyright 2009 Copenhagen

© Copyright 2009 Cracker Barrel

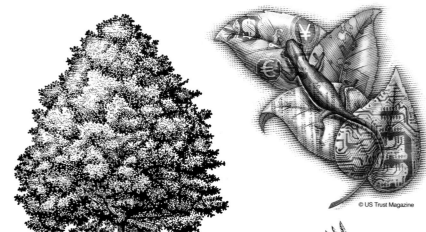

© US Trust Magazine

© Greendale Farms 2009

© Copyright 2009 Church Communities

© Copyright Welch's fruit bars

© Copyright 2009 White House Historical Association

Garden *of* Life

© Copyright 2009 Acorn

© St. Timothy's School 2009

© Iron Hill Brewery 2008

© Bear Town Bistro 2009

© Craker Barrel 2009

© Copyright 2009 Hardee's

© 2009 SLS Hotels Logo / see animation: www.slshotels.com

© Frank Sinatra / scratchboard engraving

© Copyright sailing vessel / scratchboard engraving

● BENJAMINFRETWELL.COM 415-255-6211

Great Events of the Old Testament

Illustration by Bot Roda
© 2008 CYMG
www.catholicyouth.org

BOT RODA

717-393-1406

www.botroda.com ● botroda@comcast.net

Illustration & Design **www.catmacinnes.com**
info@catmacinnes.com +61 418 354 439

I'M ON A WHISKEY DIET. I'VE LOST THREE DAYS ALREADY!
Tommy Cooper

everything in life should match

WINSTON NOGAI DESIGN

JEANNIE WINSTON   Tel: 310 458 1250   artbean@gmail.com   www.jeanniewinston.com

bellocchioillustration @ gmail.com
bellocchioIllustration . com

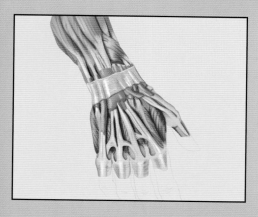
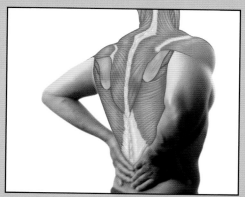
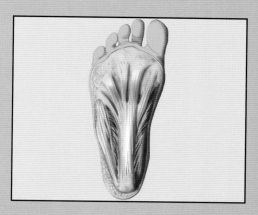

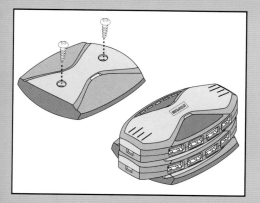
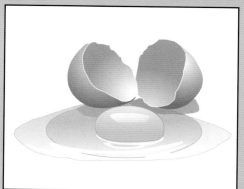
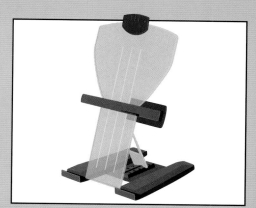

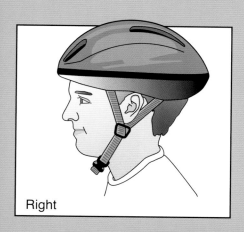

Right

Wrong

GARY E. KOEPPEL

Medical, Product and Technical Illustration

www.garykoeppel.com   **gary@garykoeppel.com**   **617•323•3862**

www.KellieLewis.com

CHARACTER DESIGN~ILLUSTRATION~STORYBOARDS

KELLIE@KELLIELEWIS.COM

THE Jockey JOURNAL

Heh

My Latest Grievance

Sluggers

Zero

Gaiters

Kinda Good

Dork

Whippets

Pfft!

Animation

Revelation

NEWS FROM LAKE WOBEGON

Two for the Road

Pant

Sins

Pop Cap

Stewardess

MoFi

Dawn McCoy

Hee Won

Gale's Garage

Geek

Mark Simonson
STUDIO
WWW.MS-STUDIO.COM • 651-307-7491

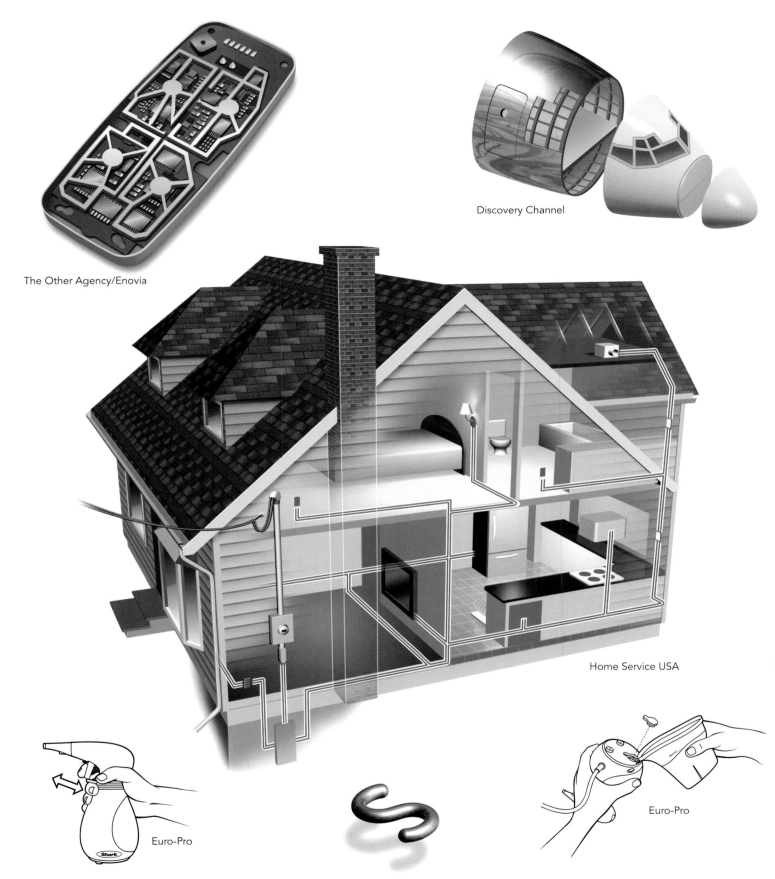

The Other Agency/Enovia

Discovery Channel

Home Service USA

Euro-Pro

Euro-Pro

STUDIO SAYERS

ILLUSTRATION · INFOGRAPHICS · DIAGRAMS · ANIMATION

Curtis Sayers 20 Mossfield Road, Waban, MA 02468 617.947.2720 curtis@studiosayers.com www.studiosayers.com

G²

UNION PACIFIC
808

UNION PACIFIC
ROCKY MOUNTAIN
Nat'l

PLEASANT SPRINGS CO

Glenn Gustafson
STUDIO: 630.947.2785

ggustafson2@yahoo.com
www.glenngustafson.com

WWW.CHADJSHAFFER.COM

631-871-4725

CHAD J. SHAFFER

WWW.CHADJSHAFFER.COM

631-871-4725

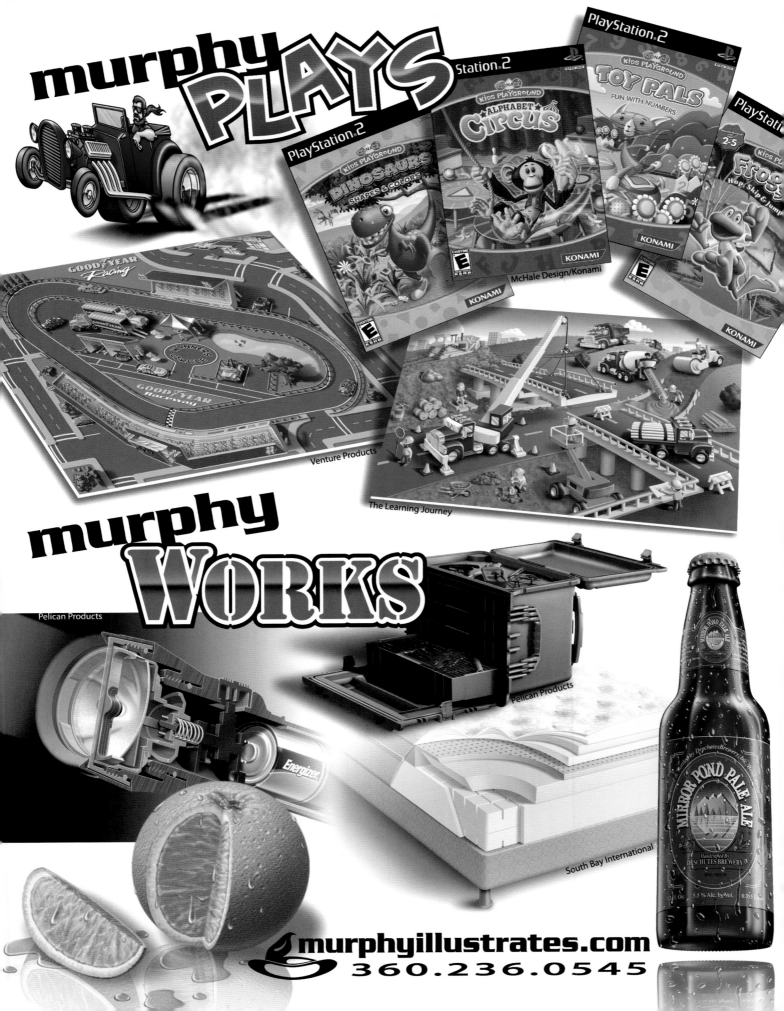

murphy PLAYS

PlayStation 2

PlayStation 2

PlayStation 2

PlayStation 2

KONAMI KIDS PLAYGROUND
DINOSAURS
SHAPES & COLORS

KONAMI KIDS PLAYGROUND
ALPHABET CIRCUS

KONAMI KIDS PLAYGROUND
TOY PALS
FUN WITH NUMBERS

KIDS PLAYGROUND
Frogs
Hop, Skip & Jump
2-5

KONAMI

KONAMI

KONAMI

McHale Design/Konami

GOOD YEAR Racing

WINNERS CIRCLE

GOOD YEAR Raceway

Venture Products

The Learning Journey

murphy WORKS

Pelican Products

Energizer

Pelican Products

South Bay International

MIRROR POND PALE ALE
Handcrafted By
DESCHUTES BREWERY
5.5 % Alc. by Vol.

murphyillustrates.com
360.236.0545

Christy Beckwith Illustration

www.cbeckwith.com   Christy@cbeckwith.com   616-633-0767

airlie
anderson
illustration

www.airlieanderson.net

airlie@airlieanderson.net

415 ☆ 425 ☆ 8406

Tammy Yee

Phone: 808-358-0210

Email: yeeart@hawaiiantel.net

www.tammyyee.com

DIGITAL AND TRADITIONAL ILLUSTRATION • LAYOUT • GRAPHICS • LOGOS • APPAREL • AUTOMOTIVE DESIGN

© Warner Bros.

ALVAREZ illustration & design

909.338.0500 studio
951.314.6359 cell

© Disney

URBANOMICS 101

"SWEETS"

Getcha Money

© Art Alvarez 2009

WANTED OUTLAW

NO.1 OUTLAW

© Art Alvarez 2009

ART ALVAREZ

aalvarez@adesign2000.com
www.adesign2000.com

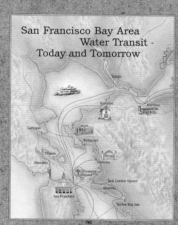

San Francisco Bay Area
Water Transit -
Today and Tomorrow

MAPS
BOTANICALS
CALLIGRAPHY

Jane Shasky
ILLUSTRATION

360.638.1276
jane@janeshasky.com
www.janeshasky.com

Jane Shasky

Fantasy

&

Children's Illustration

WESLEY LOWE

Huck Finn classic

Toronto Film Festival poster

Rudyard Kipling/U.K.

series of OZ classics

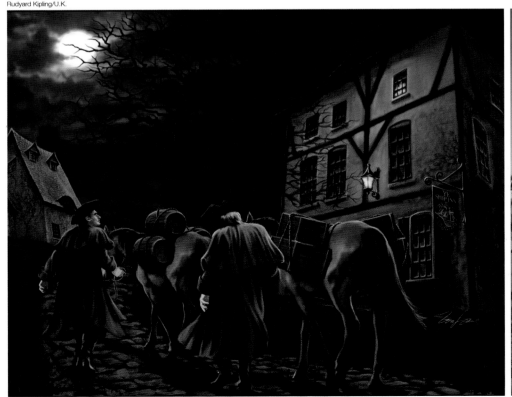

www.weslowe.com 604 885-5302

MARK EVAN WALKER   817 905 0057   mevanw@earthlink.net   markevanwalker.com

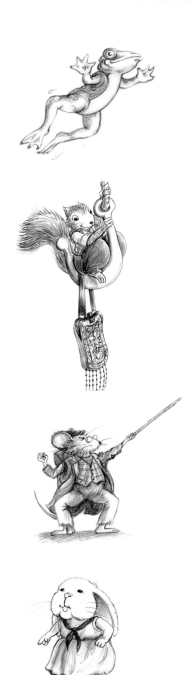

FROM **THE RUNT FARM SERIES** FOR BOOKTI MOOKTI PRESS

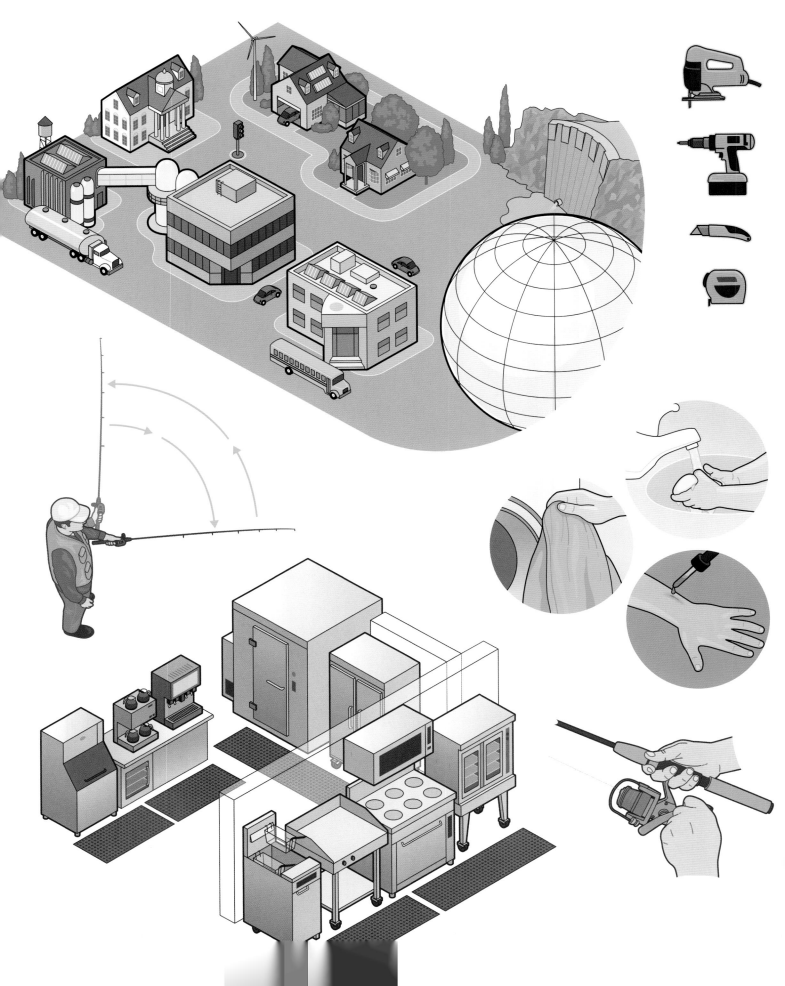

Terri Shay   terrishay.com   terrishay@copper.net

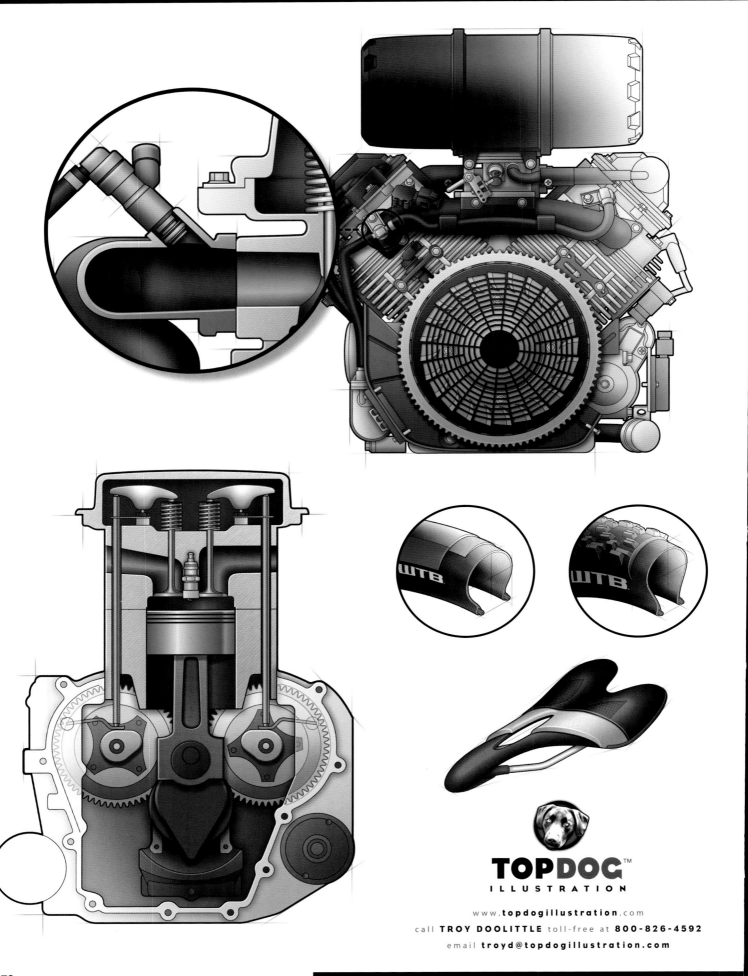

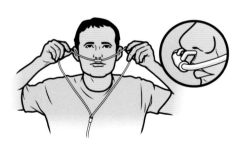
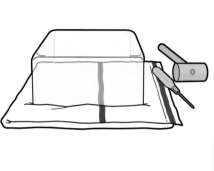
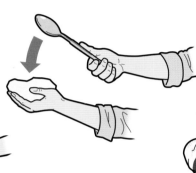

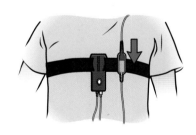

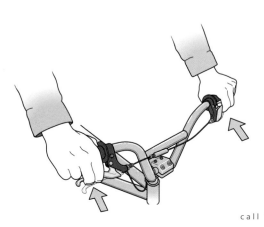

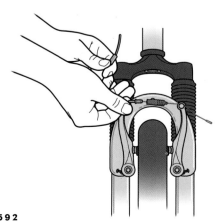

cathy
gendron

cathygendron.com

734-971-7341

cathy@cathygendron.com

FABER AND FABER ▲   ABSOLUTE MAGAZINE ▼   IEEE MAGAZINE ▲   BADGER BREWERY, DORSET UK ▼

WWW.MICKWIGGINS.COM

MICK@MICKWIGGINS.COM

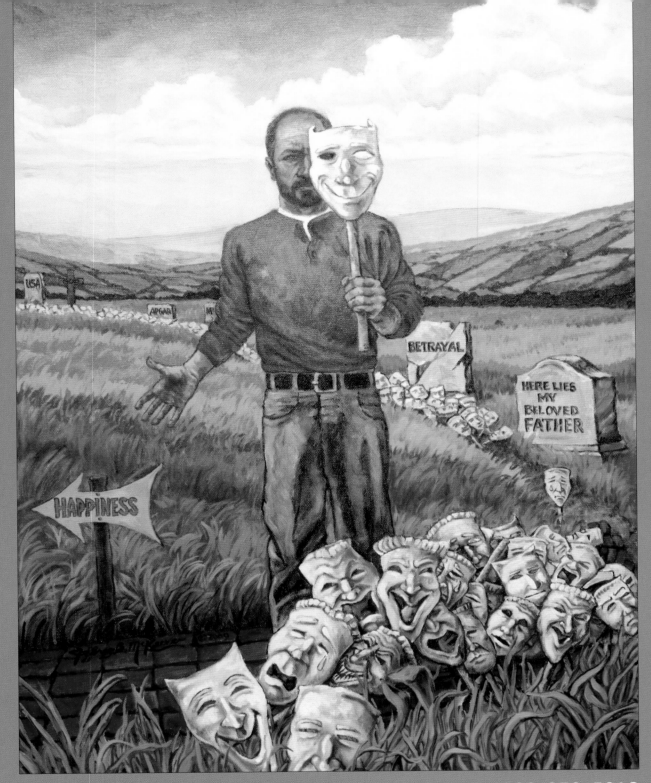

Jeffrey B. McKeever

illustration ▪ fantasy ▪ sci-fi ▪ social commentary

908-859-5812
screamingcelt@verizon.net
www.screamingceltstudio.com

BILHA GOLAN
408 · 448 · 9516

www.bilhagolan.com ❦ **bilhagolan@bilhagolan.com**

neilstewart.net
illustration • information • imagination

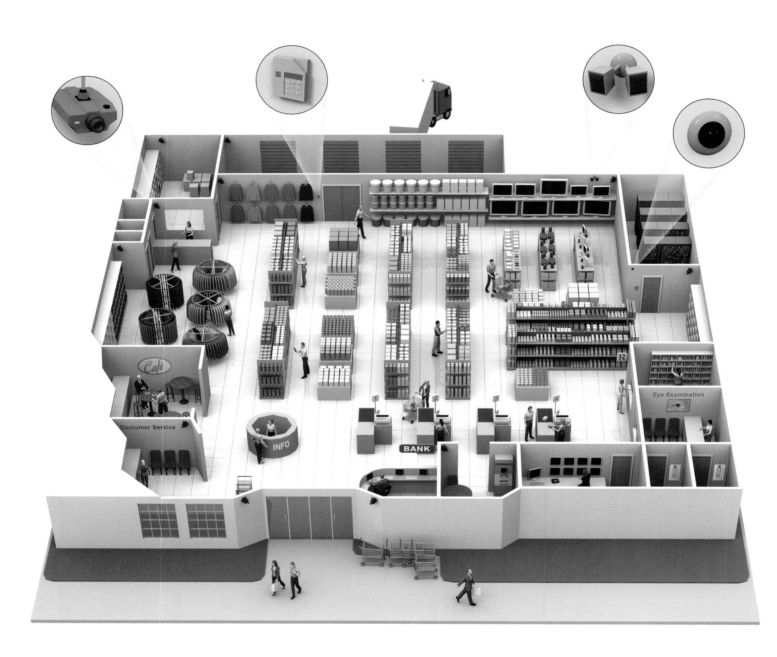

STEVE MCAFEE
813- 843-1771
s t e v e m c a f e e . c o m

ART GLAZER
2 James Road
Mt. Kisco, NY 10549
TEL: (914) 666-4554
ajglazer@optonline.net

AMY DeVOOGD

608-692-3386
www.devoogd.com
amy@devoogd.com

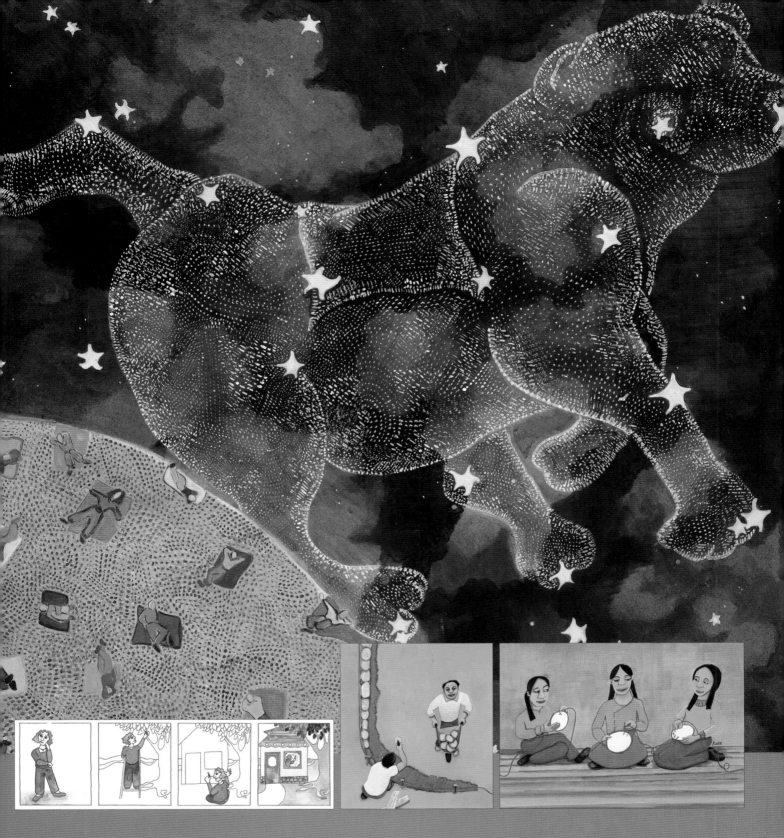

 **Kate Forman**

917 623 0106

kateillustrate@aol.com

www.kateforman.com

Ed Bray . Illustration

Comps
Storyboards
Childrens
Advertising
Editorial
Product

159 Wood Street, Suite 3, Lowell, MA 01851 • Tel/Fax 978-970-0558 Cell 651-587-0099

www.edbrayillustrations.com
edbrayillustration@verizon.net

J.DAVID McKENNEY

-917.854.2415-

Halsted Craig Hannah

Comp, McCann Erickson "Gears of War 2"

Concept art for Pixar wrap party "UP"

Sony Pictures "RENT" set illustration

"MILK" Directed by Gus Van Sant, scenic backdrop illustration

TOSCA

DON GIOVANI

"MILK" Directed by Gus Van Sant, scenic backdrop illustration

WWW.HCHANNAH.COM   (415) 823-0843   HCHANNAH@MAC.COM

FLAVORS
OF PHOENIX 2009

3...2...1... BLAST OFF
to NASA
JPL
JET PROPULSION LABORATORY
USA

Fun for the Whole Family!
Pasadena, California

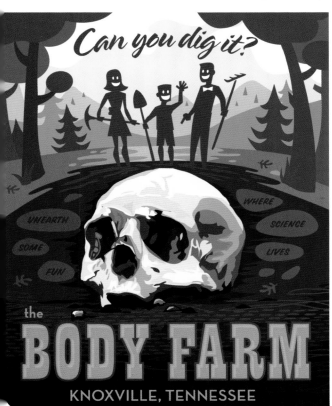

Can you dig it?

UNEARTH
SOME
FUN
WHERE
SCIENCE
LIVES

the
BODY FARM
KNOXVILLE, TENNESSEE

TSUNAMI!
RESEARCH FACILITY

CORVALLIS, OREGON

trapdoor
studio

Jonathan Arvizu
www.trapdoorstudio.com
602.330.2021

Terry Paczko 216 447 8864 • e-mail: terrypaczko@ameritech.net • www.terrypaczko.com • www.directoryofillustration.com/terrypaczko

GREG PAPROCKI

ILLUSTRATION & DESIGN

GREGPAPROCKI.COM
GPAPROCKI@COX.NET
(402)932-0722

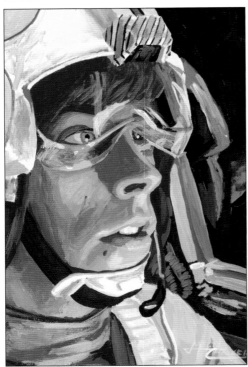

daryll collins humorous illustration

513.683-9335   daryll@daryllcollins.com   www.daryllcollins.com

Bill Otersen
850-877-9712
562 Gem Terrace Tallahassee, FL 32305

stupidstudio●com▶
bill@stupidstudio.com

George Middleton Illustration
www.georgemiddleton.com
(978) 369-0876

EVER HAVE THE FEELING YOU'RE BEING STARED AT?

SIMON DUPUIS   514.608.4218   WWW.ILLUSTROTTEUR.COM

Fifth Avenue

42ⁿᵈ Street

Grand Central

Broadway

Wall Street

Soho

image: advertisement created for the GoldToe sock company   studio: 212 477 5798   e-mail: steven@stevensalerno.com

stevensalerno.com

Darren McKee Illustration (214) 343-8766 mckee1darren@hotmail.com

DAVID RILEY
www.davidrileyillustrations.com
912.210.1278

ROB DE BANK

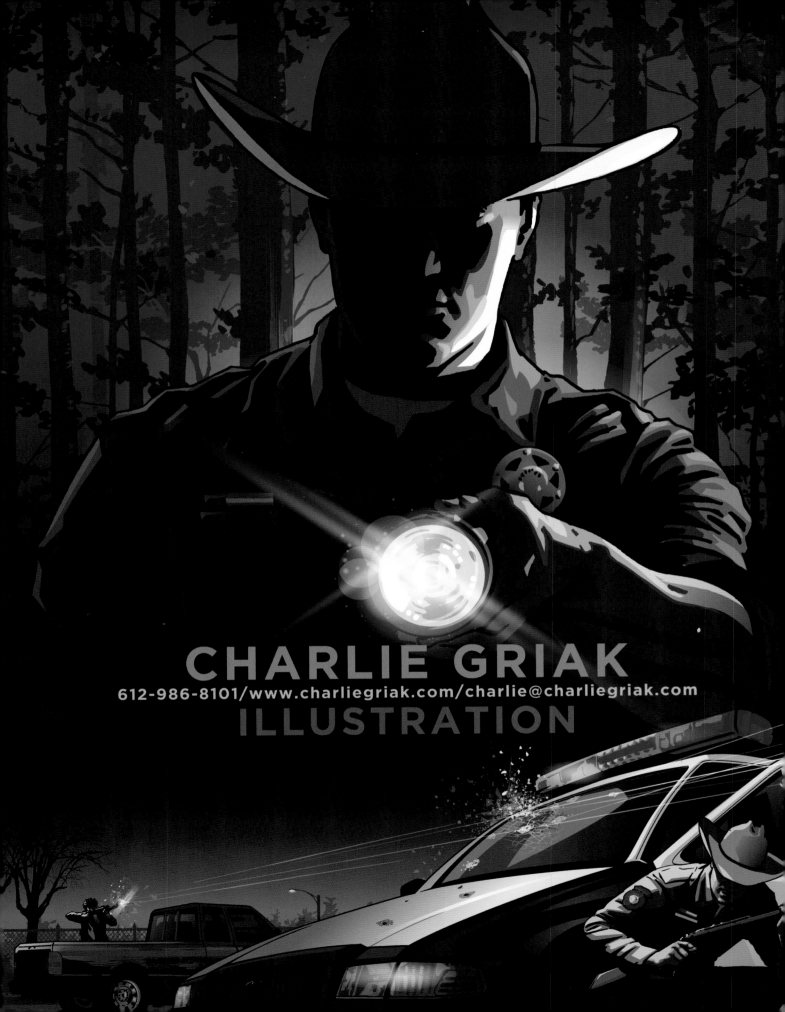

August 22nd is National Tooth Fairy Day!

While little publicized, it is nonetheless true that for every cavity, root canal, or pulled tooth, the Tooth Fairy pays one late night visit, during which she roots through couch cushions and laundry baskets, retrieving loose change from our less dentally fastidious populace. Every 22nd of August, she balances her books and purchases for herself a brand new *tutu.*

LISA FALKENSTERN

Califon Design

To view more work, see Graphics Artists Guild Directory of Illustration Vol. 12-25

904 RAVINE ROAD, CALIFON, NJ 07830
lisafalkenstern.com
Phone: (908) 832-5789 / Email: lisa@lisafalkenstern.com

905·567·1493 · Robert Johannsen
www.robertjohannsen.com · robert@robertjohannsen.com

Water Adventures Around the World

Story by Sandy Koerner, Colin Murcray & Gay Porter De Nileon
Illustrations by Lisa Tarr

American Water Works Association

Snails on Spaghetti

The Collection

Advertising Poster

www.tarrart.com **Lisa Tarr** lisa@tarrart.com

303.915.5519

'The Twelve Days of Christmas.' Comm. by Gisela Graham Ltd.

'Ram and Sita.' Comm. by Belitha Press.

'Noah's Ark.' Comm. by PR Design.

'The Three Kings.' Private Comm.

JANE TATTERSFIELD Tel: 01144 7980 122515 / 01144 1306 739440. web: www.janetattersfield.co.uk email: jtattersfield@me.com

410

Robert L. Prince   972-491-6779   robertlprince.com

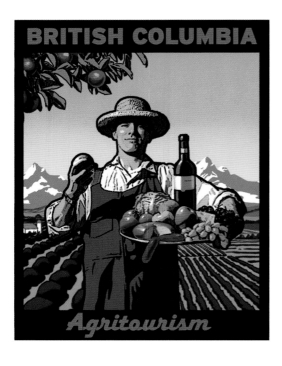

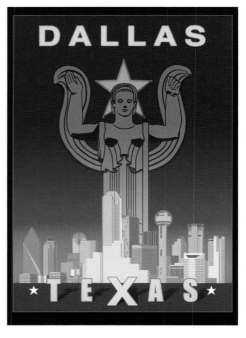
412

CHILDREN'S TEEN WOMEN FASHION ILLUSTRATOR
RHIANNON CUNAG

www.rhiannoncunag.com /// rhiannoncunag@gmail.com /// 602.466.8783

Bill Jaynes Illustration

billjaynes.com / 2924 Ostrom Ave. Long Beach, California 90815 / willieworks@billjaynes.com / ph.562-760-1811 / billjaynes.blogspot.com

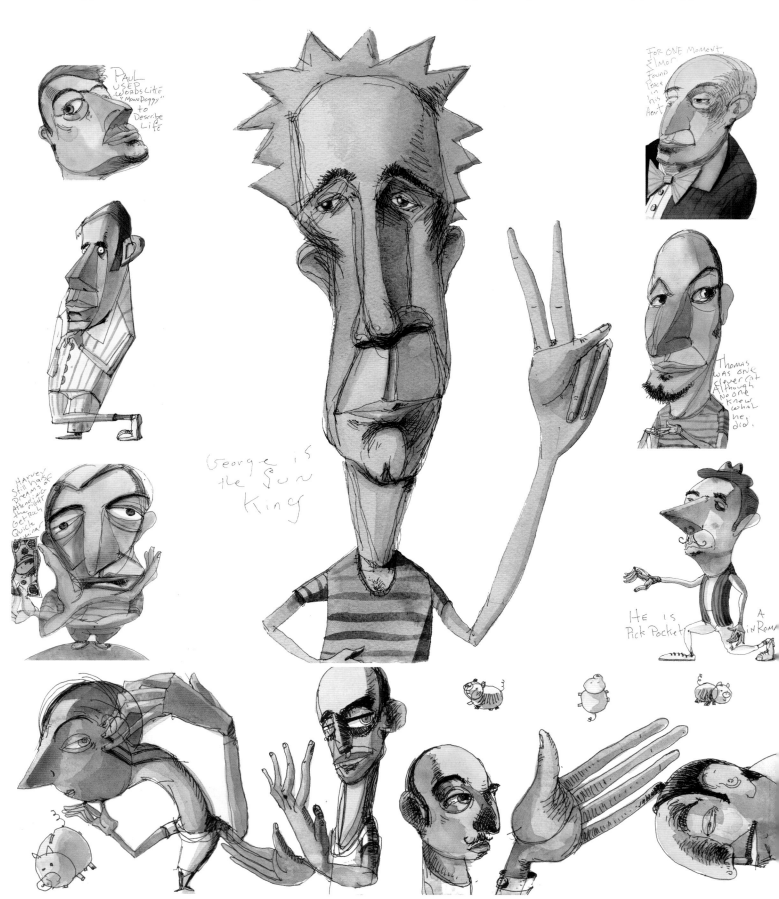

billjaynes.com / 2924 Ostrom Ave. Long Beach, California 90815 / willieworks@billjaynes.com / ph.562-760-1811 / billjaynes.blogspot.com

414

SORRY!
The Game of Sweet Revenge

The Original of CONNECT 4

SORRY!
electronic talking CARD REVENGE

SORRY!
Sliders

PIXEL PUSHERS DESIGN

telephone : 972.814.0690 | www.pixelpushersdesign.com

Terri Cook
Promotion Product Packaging

Your advantage in a competitive marketplace

san francisco zoo

CELADON

Design

celadondesign@cfl.rr.com

407-461-7964

Illustration Portfolio   www.terricook-art.com

For Product Graphics   www.celadonart.net

 TONY **POUNCEY**

illustrator & designer, is now with

big eye design

tel: 770·587·4456
email: tony@bigeyedesign.com
web: www.bigeyedesign.com

www.bigeyedesign.com

417

richardsmyth.net

Louise Comfort   Louisecomfort1@yahoo.co.uk

www.louisecomfort.co.uk

RON
TANOVITZ

WOOD ENGRAVING

PHONE: 510.339.0182   FAX: 510.654.6631   PORTFOLIO: stcreative.com/ron.html   EMAIL: ron@stcreative.com

PICTORIAL MAPS

PHONE: 510.339.0182   FAX: 510.654.6631   PORTFOLIO: stcreative.com/eve.html   EMAIL: eve@stcreative.com

Ariane Elsammak

www.artbyari.com~info@artbyari.com~908·464·5866

jennifer hewitson

1145 wotan drive | encinitas | california 92024 | 760.944.6154 | www.theispot.com/artist/jhewitson

Matt Kania
Map Illustrations

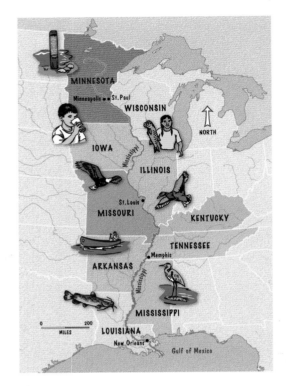

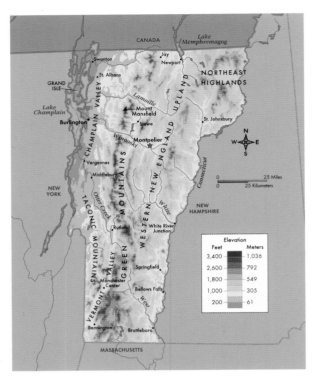

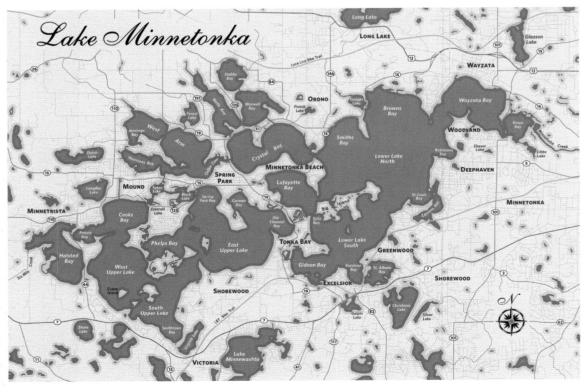

424

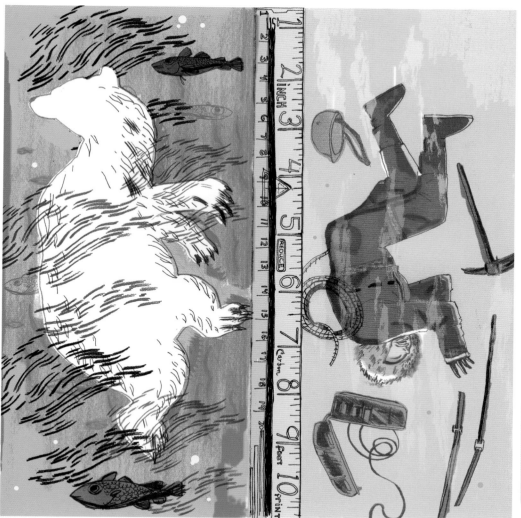

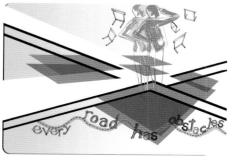

"Crime of Passion"
illustration about mistakes made
and love lost.

"Every Road Has Obstacles"
a piece dealing with hurdles in every
direction.

"She Came in with the Wind"
An illustration about the significance of a friend

"Man Made Melting"
illustration deals with scientist who risk their lives to measure the growing loss of
arctic habitats.

Art on Record Show *APW Gallery - New York*

STEVEN LAWRENCE

WWW.STLAWRENCEART.COM
stevenarts82@gmail.com   directory of Illustration 26

t a d   h e r r

Stephan & Herr

Illustration and Graphic Design

717·426·2939   www.stephanherr.com   Directory of Illustration 16-25

Phone: 810-797-5001

john@grafixjam.com

www.grafixjam.com

John Rios

JENN MCGILL

jennmcgill.com

jenn@jennmcgill.com
360.293.6359

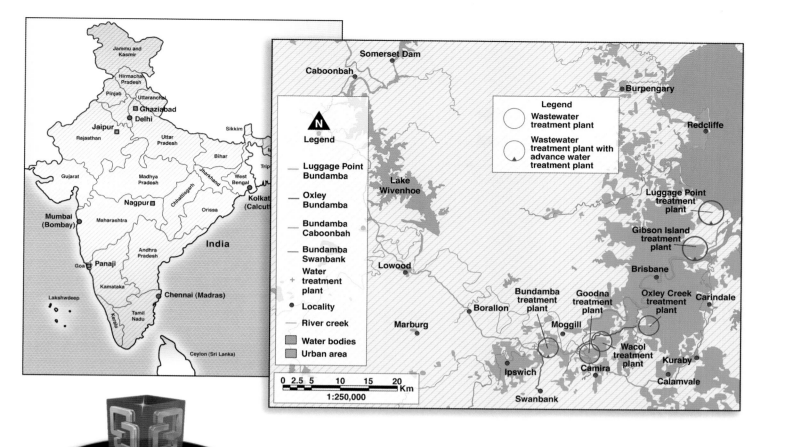

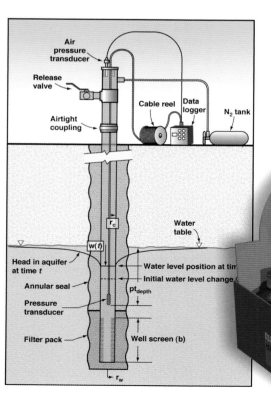

F R A N K C E R U L L I

JOHN STEVEN GURNEY

710 Western Avenue, Brattleboro, Vermont 05301   802-258-2654   johnsgurney@comcast.net   johnstevengurney.com

WIL YEE
illustrator of sorts

Wanna Play?

www.wilyee.com
wil@wilyee.com
403.836.9459

tom hennessy
· www.hennessyart.com · tom@hennessyart.com · Tel: 415 388-7959

GARY NEWMAN
ILLUSTRATION

www.gary-newman.com   call: +44 (0)7903-584-937   email: info@gary-newman.com

Recent Clients include **Disney Gillette L'Oreal Mattel SONY** and **Virgin**

View full and extensive portfolio on-line at
www.gary-newman.com

URBAN
SKIING
Blown Away Waves

www.gary-newman.com

ILLUSTRATIONS by **Jason Abbott** | **678.642.2886**

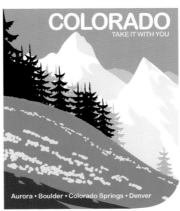

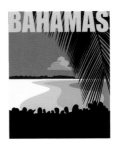

ADAM BENTON
3D & 2D DIGITAL ILLUSTRATION

editorial • advertising
educational • scientific
concept • visualisation
futuristic • sci-fi
product • design
film • cinematics • matte
animation • motion-graphics

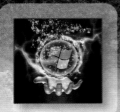

bruce dunlap

palm springs, california

760.325.0463
be2dunlap@aol.com
www.directoryofillustration.com/brucedunlap

carolina@hintstudio.com

phone: 401-286-1794

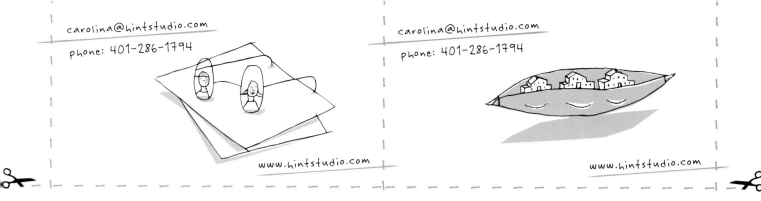

www.hintstudio.com

carolina@hintstudio.com

phone: 401-286-1794

www.hintstudio.com

Carolina Arentsen
www.hintstudio.com

29 Ogden Street, Providence RI 02906   p: 401-286-1794   e: carolina@hintstudio.com

Illustrations created for, Annenberg Institute for School Reform at Brown University, Voices in Urban Education (V.U.E)
A quarterly book distributed to public schools, throughout the United States, with articles based on studies focusing on
problem solving and overall improvement of public schools, especially in inner city environments.

Digital illustration for advertising packaging and publishing. Based in the UK, Vincent and Lesley Wakerley are professional and experienced illustrators working for advertising agencies and design studios around the world. Specialising in food, drink, scenic and figurative images.

Contact Vincent or Lesley on
Tel; +44 (0)1205 761 79
Email; vincentwakerley@btinternet.com
lesleywakerley@btinternet.com

See more images at
www.id2-studio.com

iD2

inkyboy.com

john.inkyboy@gmail.com

630.244.4858

john aardema

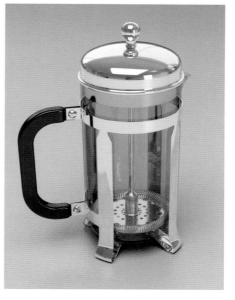

Scott Angle

www.scottangle.com

email:sangle@socal.rr.com
ph.714-625-7120

kath walker illustration

www.kathwalker.co.uk . info@kathwalker.co.uk . +44 (0)1772 712154

Barbara Hicks

204-256-3718 • bhgs@shaw.ca • www.hickspix.ca

Watercolour: *Water Quality Handbook* - Government of Manitoba, Galapagos Island project, and *All I Wanted Was a Dog!* children's picture book.
Digital: Education Calendar, Cancer Care Manitoba poster and Healthy Child booklet.

447

karl huber - illustration
1404 monterey st.#3 pittsburgh, PA 15212
412 874-8166 kfhuber@hotmail.com

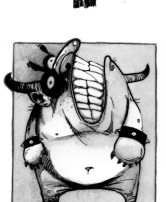

kerrtoons@cox.net
(402) 384-8845
www.tomkerrart.com

They're stuffed with the feathers
that come from a bird,
Which molts once a year
every April the third.
These feathers (so light
that no measure's been found),
Take nearly ten months
to descend to the ground.
With feathers that light
from a bird that's so small,
It's a wonder we've got any
pillows at all.
But the men Dinsmore
hires are patient you see,
And brave, I might add,
to stand under that tree.

859·619·8379
britt spencer
britt@brittspencer.com

www.brittspencer.com

Brie Spangler
· illustrator ·
www.briespangler.com
917.592.8117

Illustration and Design by **Kevin Wood**

Funkybat.com

3511 Springlake Dr.   San Leandro, CA 94578

510-471-1265   kevcreative@funkybat.com

www.lynnrowereed.com
lynn@lynnrowereed.com
260.422.1558

LYNN rowe REED

NATALIE TONEY

www.natalietoney.com

natalietoney@gmail.com

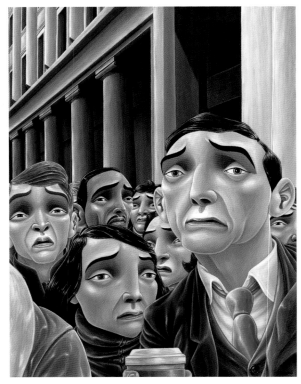

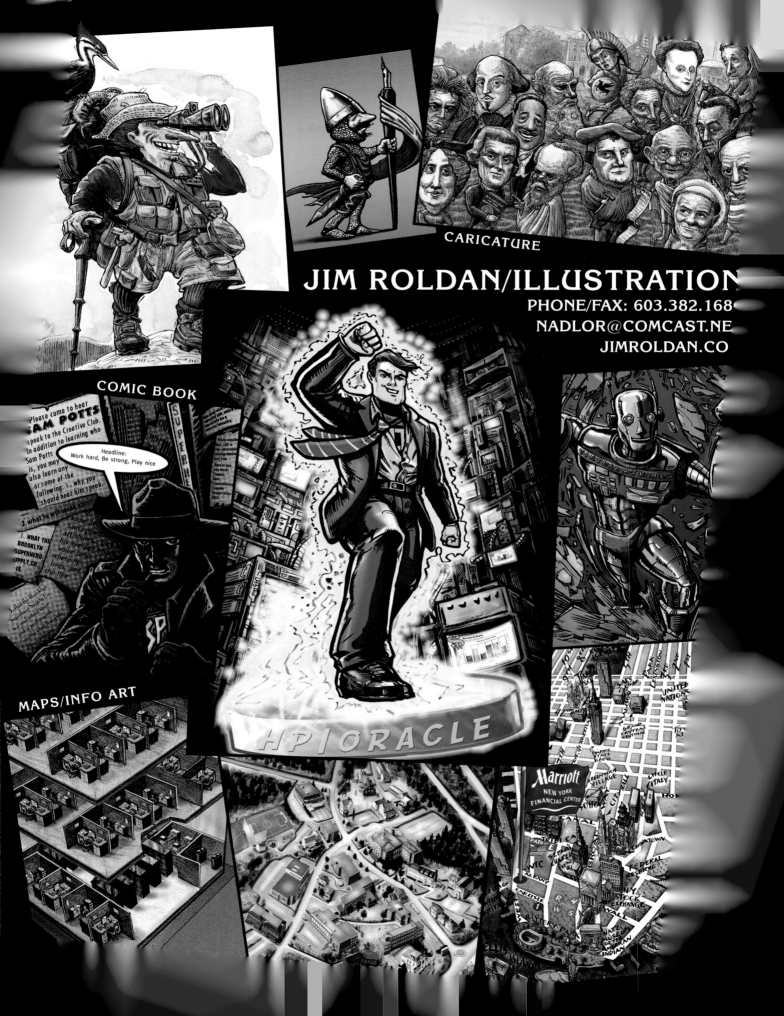

CARICATURE

JIM ROLDAN/ILLUSTRATION
PHONE/FAX: 603.382.168
NADLOR@COMCAST.NE
JIMROLDAN.CO

COMIC BOOK

MAPS/INFO ART

kristian
bauthus
illustration

to view more illustrations or client list, visit:

kristian@kbauthus.com
(416).579.4479

www.kbauthus.com

cartoon illustration for point of sale packaging advertising editorial character development

David Banks

phn +44 (0) 1206 520 792 cell +44 (0) 781 782 6375
email david@bankscartoons.com web www.bankscartoons.com

Carol Coogan

info@carolcoogandesign.com

518·436·4929

Sarah Edgar
Illustrator/Graphic Artist

62-65 Saunders Street #3C
Rego Park, New York 11374
(718) 896-2812

www.sarahedgar.com

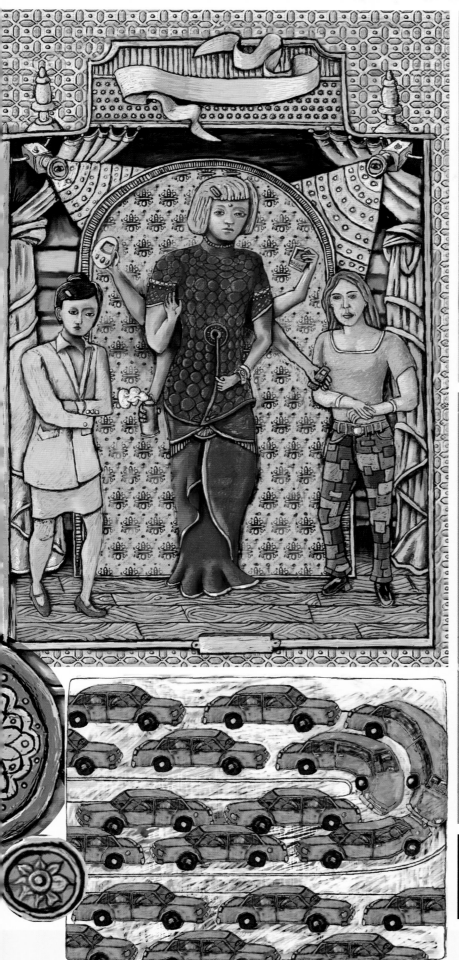

Chris S. Johnson
Email: cj@csj2.com
ph: 928-380-9100

CSJ2
ILLUSTRATION FLAGSTAFF, AZ

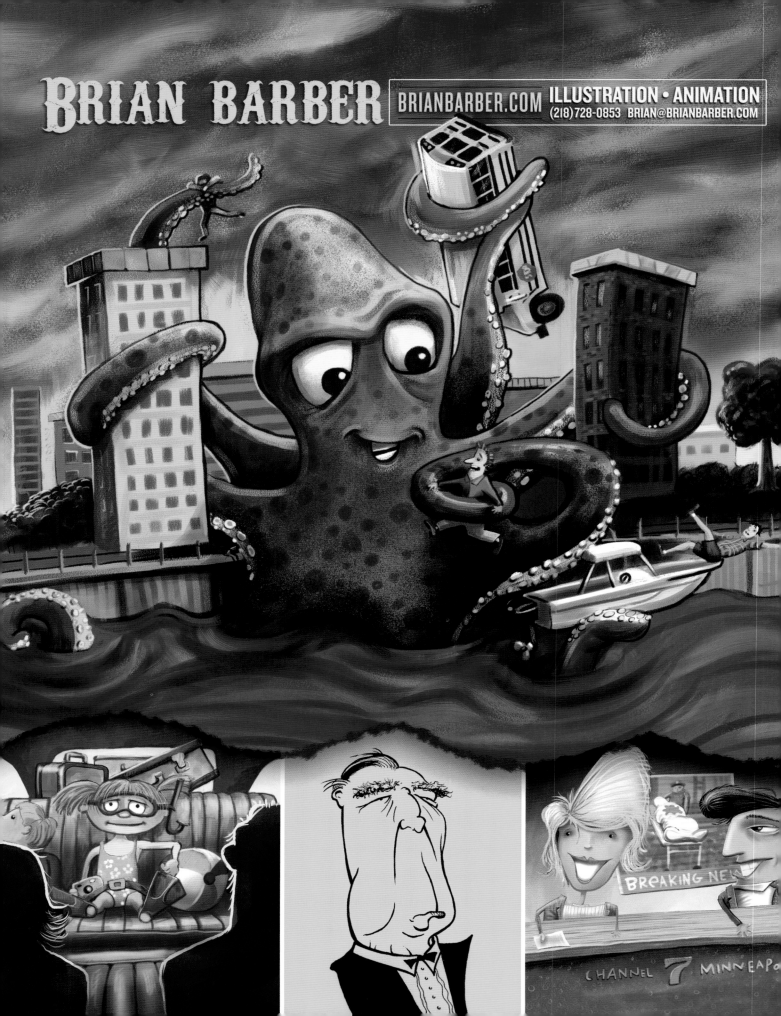

BRIAN BARBER · BRIANBARBER.COM · ILLUSTRATION · ANIMATION · (218) 728-0853 · BRIAN@BRIANBARBER.COM

RIESER

william rieser | illustration | 415 389 0332

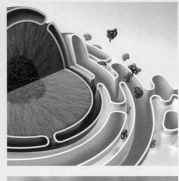

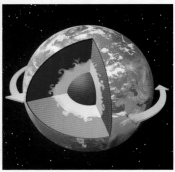

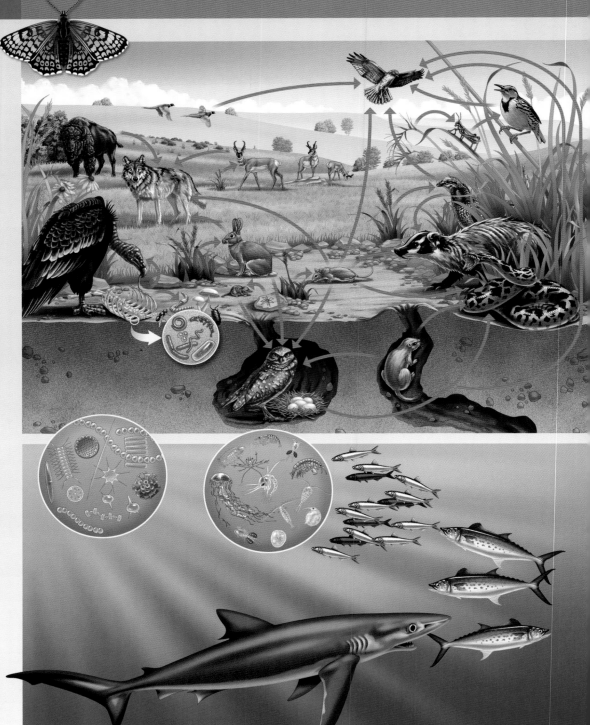

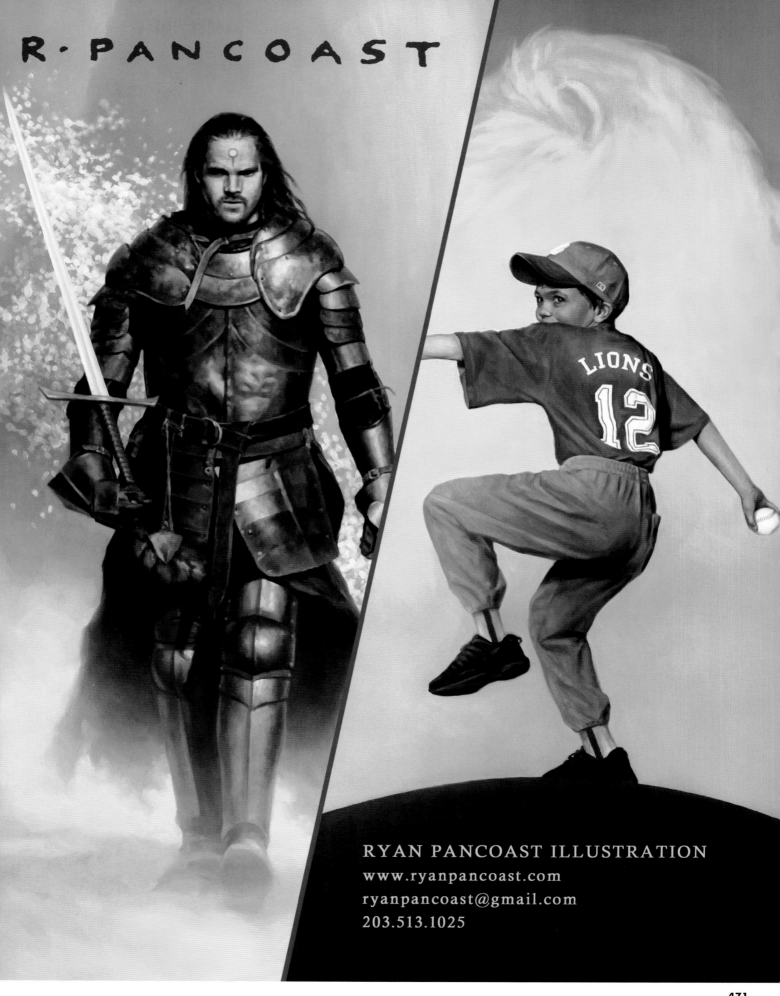

Wynken Blynken Nod

Carolyn Karasek Stu

(618)939-9884, (618)593-87

Carolynkarasekstudio.cor

Ken Spengler

Spengler Creations Inc.
www.kenspengler.com
ph (916) 441-1932 / cell (916) 296-6613
email: ken@spenglercreations.com

Ulana Zahajkewycz

Illustration * Wooden Folk Craft

ulanaz@yahoo.com
http://ulanaland.com

717-993-6598
jim@jimstarr.com
www.jimstarr.com

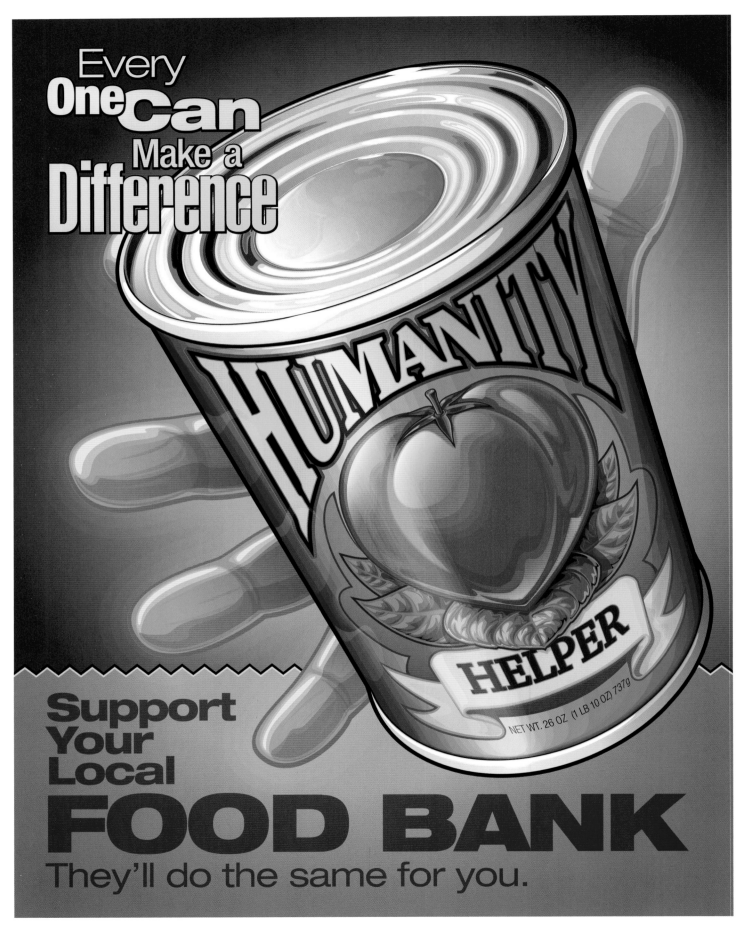

Every
OneCan
Make a
Difference

HUMANITY

HELPER

NET WT. 26 OZ. (1 LB 10 OZ) 737g

**Support
Your
Local**
FOOD BANK
They'll do the same for you.

Chris Lensch
www.chrislensch.com
phone:231-392-9205

SHAWN FINLEY.com

Jeff Grunewald
digital illustration
773-281-5284
www.jeffgrunewald.com

Rock the Runway

the Cat's meow! the cat's meow! the cat's me 's meou meou! meow! the Ca the Ca eow! the cats meow! cat's meou the cat's meow! th cats meow! cat's meow! the cat's w

leather and lace...

skin and bare it!

DABERKO DESIGN
TYPOGRAPHY
EDITORIAL
PREMIUM
FASHION
BRANDING
Packaging
go Green
Books
illustration
Logos
daberkodesign.com
Seattle WA · 206-935-3656
info@daberkodesign.com

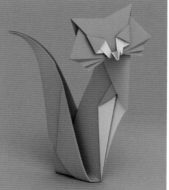

485

Super de Duper Illustration

Kristen Brennan ★ **kristy@superdeduper.net**

119 SCHOOL STREET, BALA CYNWYD, PA 19004 ★ 215-350-7854

★ **WWW.SUPERDEDUPER.net** ★

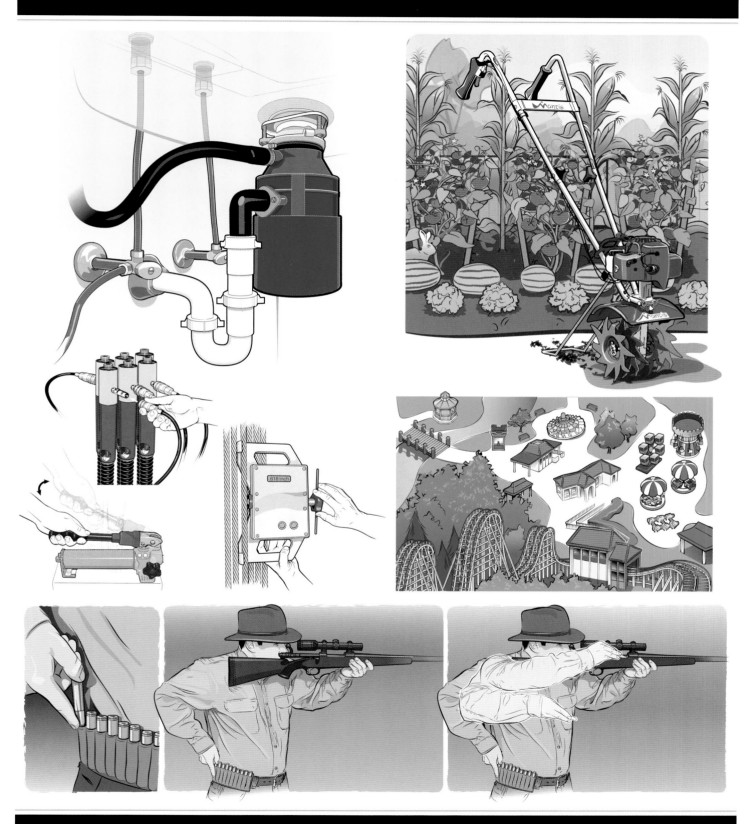

www.patrickwelsh.com • pat@patrickwelsh.com • 609-221-1030

Bryan Berry   858.748.0334
www.BryanBerryIllustration.com

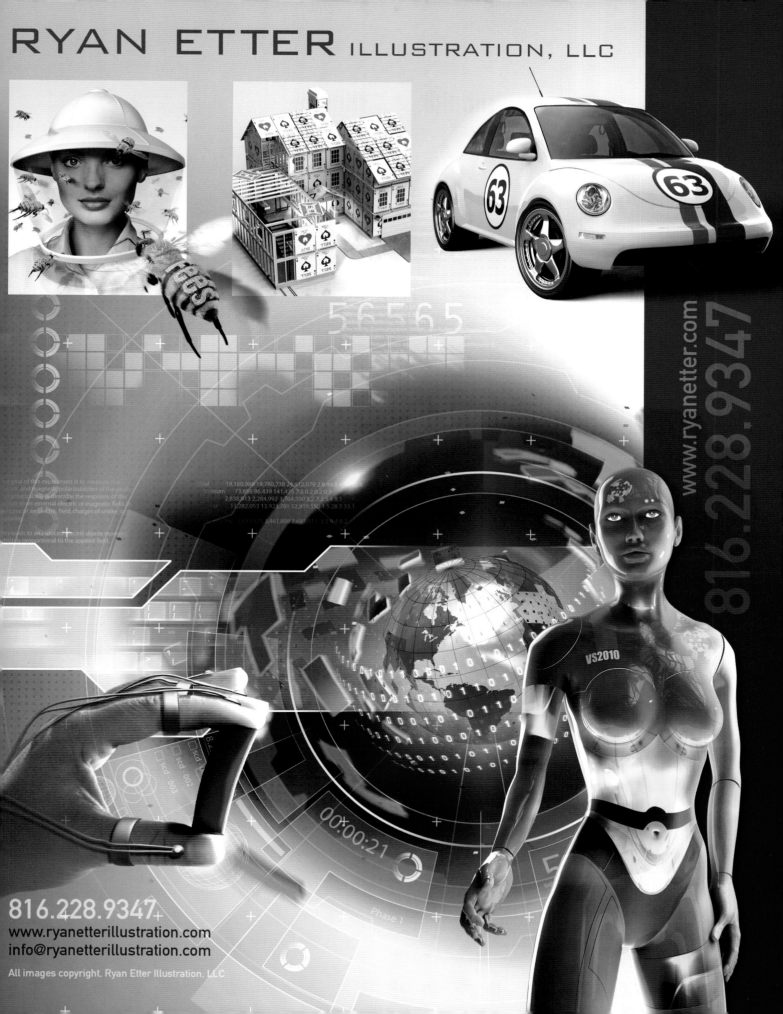

RYAN ETTER ILLUSTRATION, LLC

www.ryanetter.com

816.228.9347

816.228.9347
www.ryanetterillustration.com
info@ryanetterillustration.com

www.cjohnsonart.com   chris@cjohnsonart.com

845.548.0872

888•403•1004   F – 562•989•9539   carickature@aol.com • www.theispot.com/artist/rewing

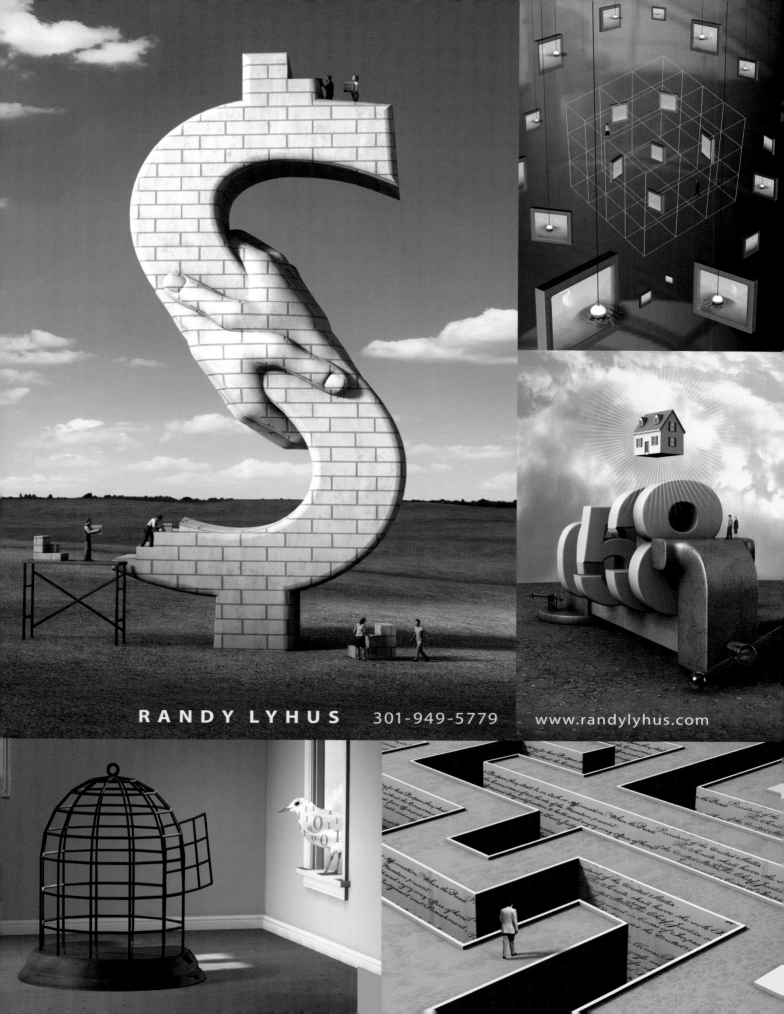

Lesley Wolf

Illustration W *Design*

lesley@wolfdesign.net • www.wolfdesign.net • 805.962.6621

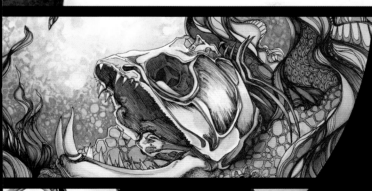

Tina Darling

Hugh D'Andrade www.hughillustration.com

npr

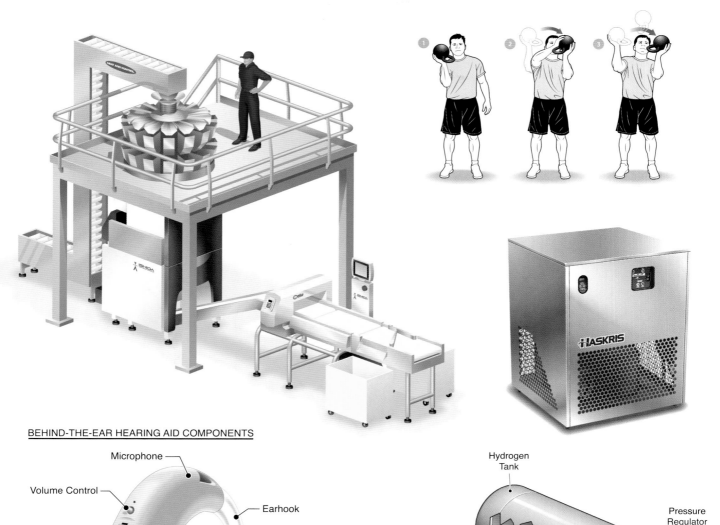

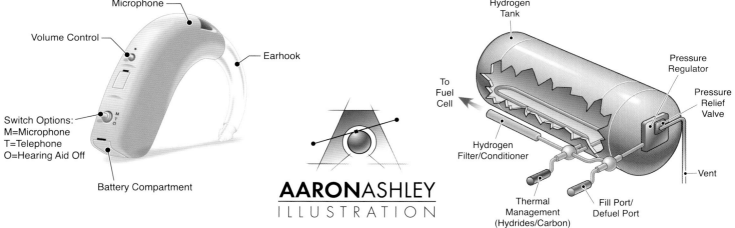

BEHIND-THE-EAR HEARING AID COMPONENTS

Microphone

Volume Control

Earhook

Switch Options:
M=Microphone
T=Telephone
O=Hearing Aid Off

Battery Compartment

AARONASHLEY
ILLUSTRATION

Hydrogen
Tank

Pressure
Regulator

Pressure
Relief
Valve

To
Fuel
Cell

Hydrogen
Filter/Conditioner

Vent

Thermal
Management
(Hydrides/Carbon)

Fill Port/
Defuel Port

James W. Elston Illustration

www.jameselston.com
james.elston@gmail.com
814-248-8396

Patrick McFarlin

PACKAGING, PUBLISHING, ADVERTISING, BRANDING

Stags' Leap Winery
Chateau Souverain Winery
Beringer Wine Estates
Meridian Winery
Quixote Winery
Brittan Vineyards
Twotone Farm Wine
Foster's Wine Estates
Sutcliffe Vineyards
585 Wine Partners
Encantado Mezcal
Williams and Sonoma
Clover Organic Diary
Art of Eating Journal
Voicebox Creative
Santa Fe Wine & Chile Fiesta
Santa Fe Opera
Oldways Preservation & Trust
Broadway Books
Gibbs-Smith Publisher
Heyday Press
Princeton University Press

Review projects at **mcfarlinoil.com/projects**
More art at **directoryofillustration.com**
e-mail: oil@newmexico.com   phone 505 983-8551

THE
NUTCRACKER

BALLET

Body Shoppe

WYOMISSING CREEK FLY SHOP

Baked.
Right.
Here.

Cabin Fever

Crystal Lake Cabin Rentals

Vacancy

vic kulihin
ILLUSTRATION

Images that inform...explaining the concept visually...transforming complexity into clarity.

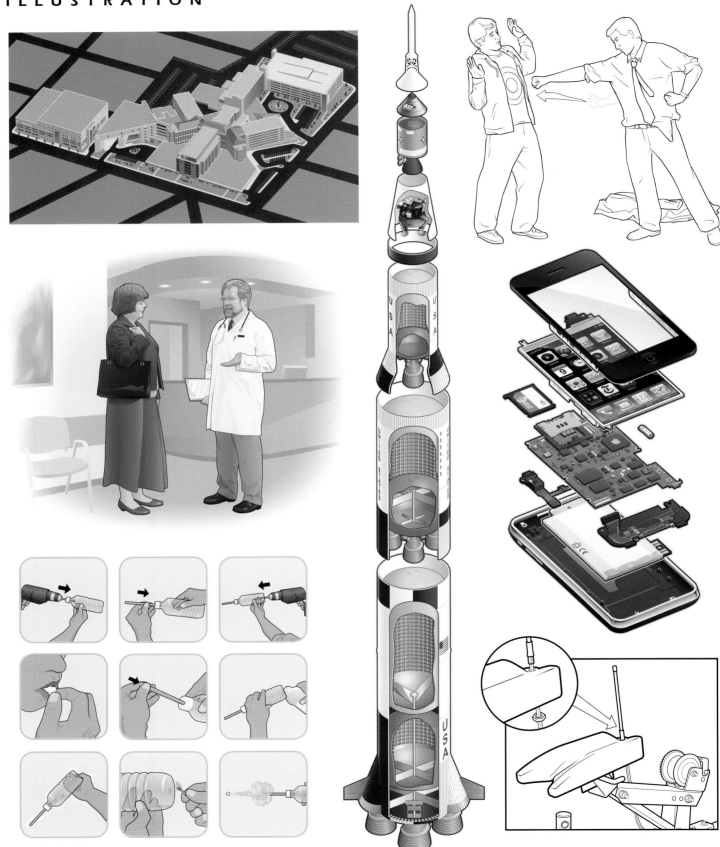

vic@vickulihinillustration.com ▪ 908.757.4678 ▪ www.vickulihinillustration.com

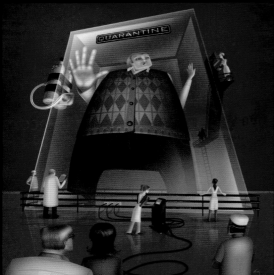

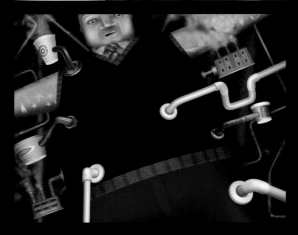

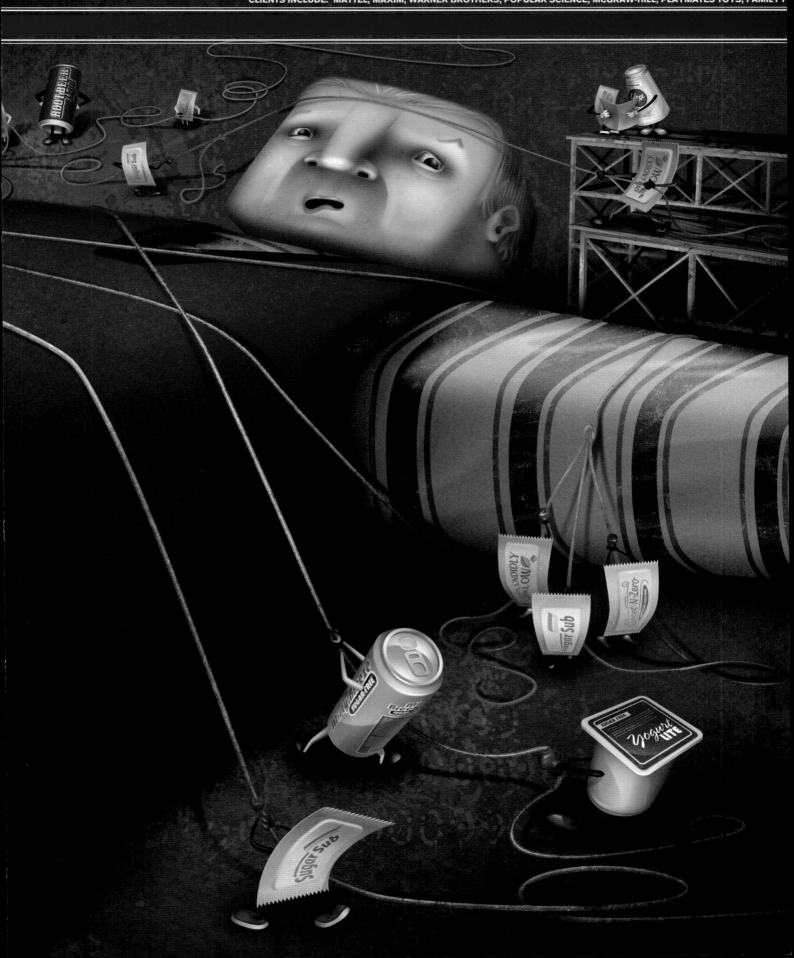

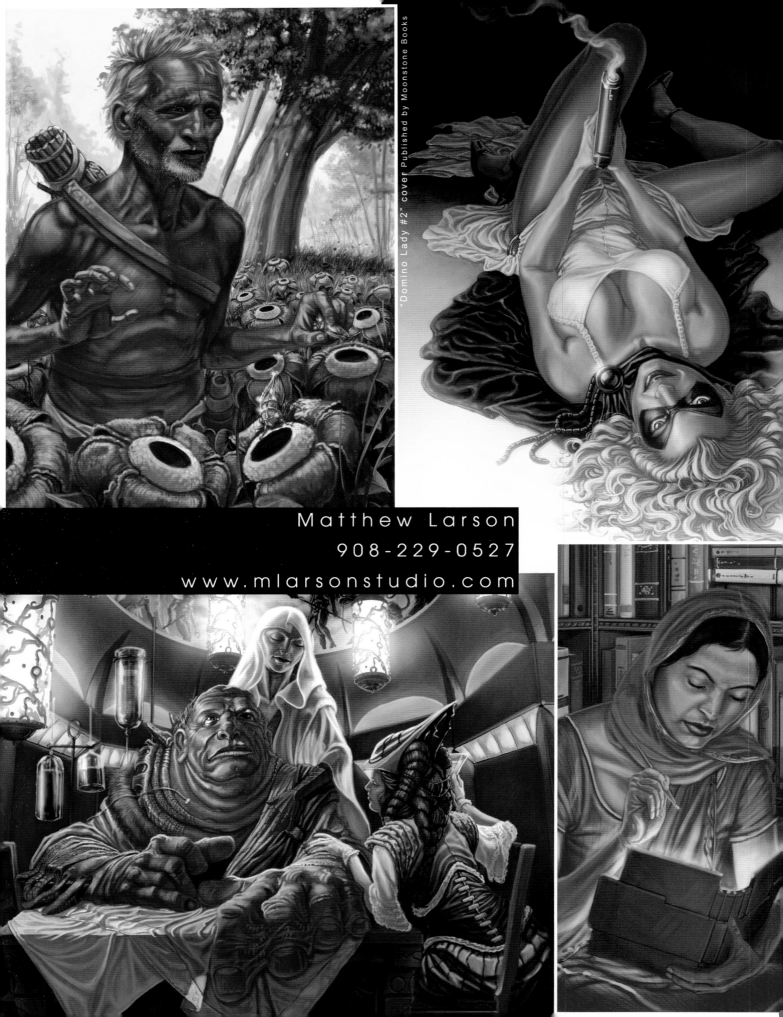

Matthew Larson
908-229-0527
www.mlarsonstudio.com

"Domino Lady #2" cover Published by Moonstone Books

leighton hubbell

ILLUSTRATION LETTERING LOGOS ICONS

brian arden wines

KOOTENAI
OLD MONTANA

UC CONSTRUCTION

BAYOU
BRASS BAND

nest | LIFE

THE SOUNDGARDEN

Zeke's Tentation

SEAPORT
SUSTAINABILITY
SYMPOSIUM

People

Guides

English translation

Buy flight

Important info

Restaurants

Shopping

Nightlife

Daytrip

Attractions

★ 2
8 9
Events

leightonhubbell.com

714.227.3457
info@leightonhubbell.com

Kathy Rusynyk

NATURE ILLUSTRATOR

kathyrusynyk.com
kathyrusynyk@zoominternet.net

Bee Happy

Bee at Happy!

Bee Happy!
PURE HONEY

orange blossom

PO BOX 323 ~ Ashland, Ohio 44805

508

ViviannaCalabria
ILLUSTRATOR
267.614.1329
stiletto_art@yahoo.com
creativehotlist.com/vcalabria
stilettoart.com
directoryofillustration.com/ViviannaCalabria

the situational fashionista in dynamic line and color

509

Dave Thorp
Design & Illustration

dave@pumpkin-guy.com

720-339-9735

Arrrrrgh!!

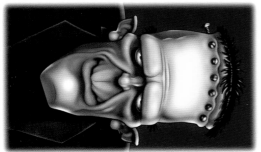

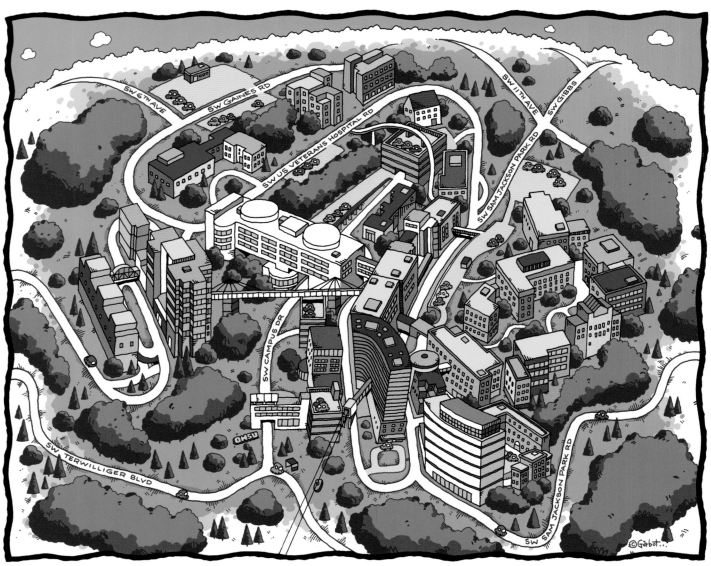

Dave Garbôt Illustration (503)579·0663 www.garbot.com

Eddie Young Illustration & Design

Eddie Young Builds Good Characters!

All images ©2009 Eddie Young Illustration & Design

Studio: 562 429-2513 web: eddieyoung.com E-mail: youngeddie@eddieyoung.com

CHOOCHLAND.COM

Judith Soderquist Cummins

550 Union Street, Brooklyn, New York 11215   Tel/Fax: 718-596-1233

Websites: www.judithcummins.com

www.directoryofillustration.com/JudithSoderquistCummins

Email: judithcummins@earthlink.net

Melissa DeSilva DeCunha

melissa.decunha@comcast.net   (617) 895-7124

www.mchillifry.com

Web design, flash animation, package design, digital illustration ...

P O I

 PLAY ODYSSEY INC www.playoi.com 310-575-0602

MADE AT
CITY WINERY
VINTAGE 2008
CABERNET
SAUVIGN...

Michael Do...

EN
FLEUR
Verbena
FRAGRANCE
DIFFUSER

Barbie™

FRANCIS
COPPOLA
PRESENTS

1997

ROSSO
CALIFORNIA RED WINE

...SENCE, PETULANT, REVOLUTION...

SOFIA
Blanc de Blancs
CALIFORNIA

Spring Fever

Feel-good fragrance
1.7 fl. oz./50 ml ℮
ORIGINS

The Art of the Brand

United States Postal Service First Class 'Love Stamp'

Jeanne Greco
CAFFE GRECO DESIGN
Logos & Lettering, Package Design, Illustration

MAKING IMAGES. IMAGE MAKING.

Call or drop a line to see what we can create for you.

jeannegreco@caffegrecodesign.com ☎ 917 574 8569

CAFFEGRECODESIGN.COM

PRICE $4.50

THE
NEW YORKER

NOV. 10, 2008

susieweber.com   2390 Highland Road • Jackson, WI 53037 • 262.677.2897

Susie Weber

award-winning illustration • calendars • greeting cards • packaging • publishing • annual reports

SOftPILL

Illustration & Design by
Grace Chen
www.Softpill.com
grace@softpill.com
510 658 3037

iLLUSTRATION

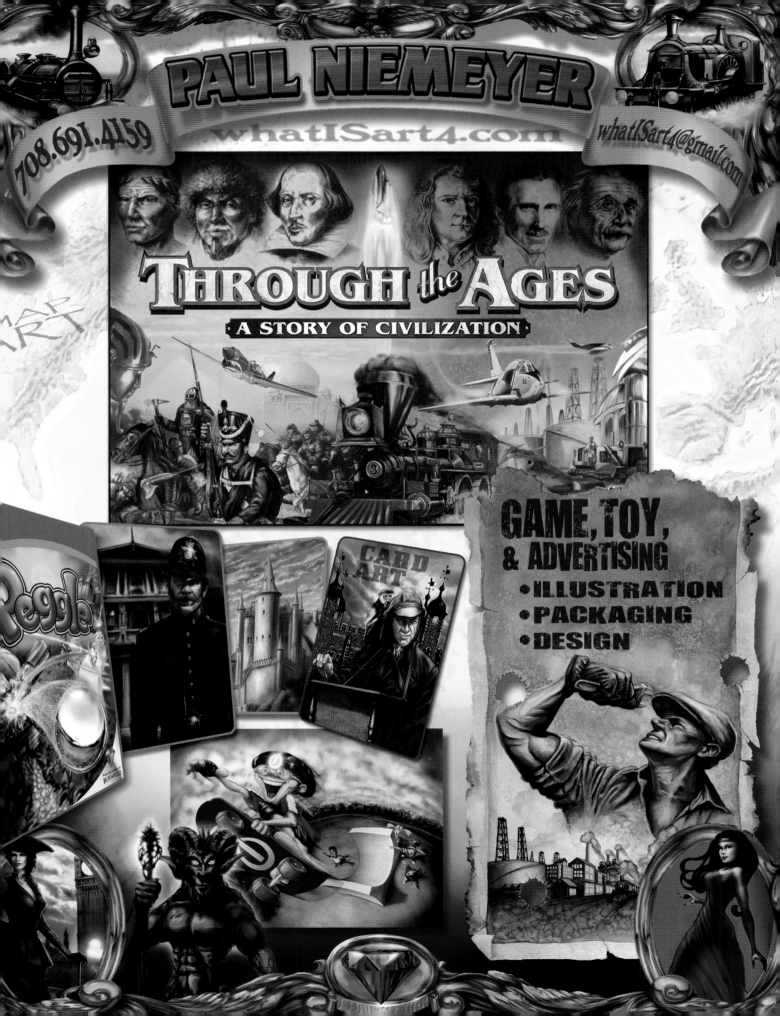

DIGITAL

TRADITIONAL

JASON M. COLE

989-493-9065

WWW.JOJAMAMIDA.COM

CARLA BAUER
WOODCUT
ILLUSTRATION

CARLA BAUER DESIGN
SUITE 1107
156 FIFTH AVENUE
NEW YORK NY 10010

T 212 807 8305
F 212 206 8005
C 646 335 5202
E carlabauer@earthlink.net

ALAN POLLACK
NEW YORK

APOLLACKSTUDIOS@ZOOM-DSL.COM

ALANPOLLACK.COM

607-532-4101

Lisa Lavoie
Illustration
(917) 531-9528
www.lisalavoie.com
lisadraws@gmail.com

Miguel Valenzuela   (626) 290-5187   www.migvalenz.com

3D Illustration
3D Animation
CAD Translation
Multimedia

3D graphics should do more than inform. They should illuminate.

Adam Questell (questell@akyudesign.com)
9911 Vogue Lane Houston, TX 77080
713.468.9595 (tel) 713.468.9597 (fax)
w w w . a k y u d e s i g n . c o m

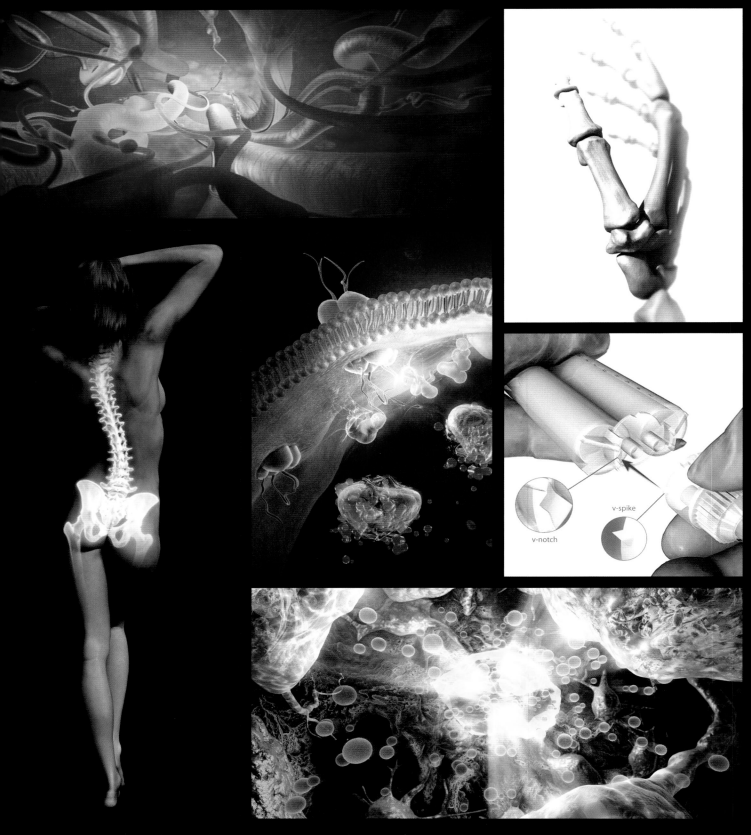

3D graphics should do more than inform. They should illuminate.

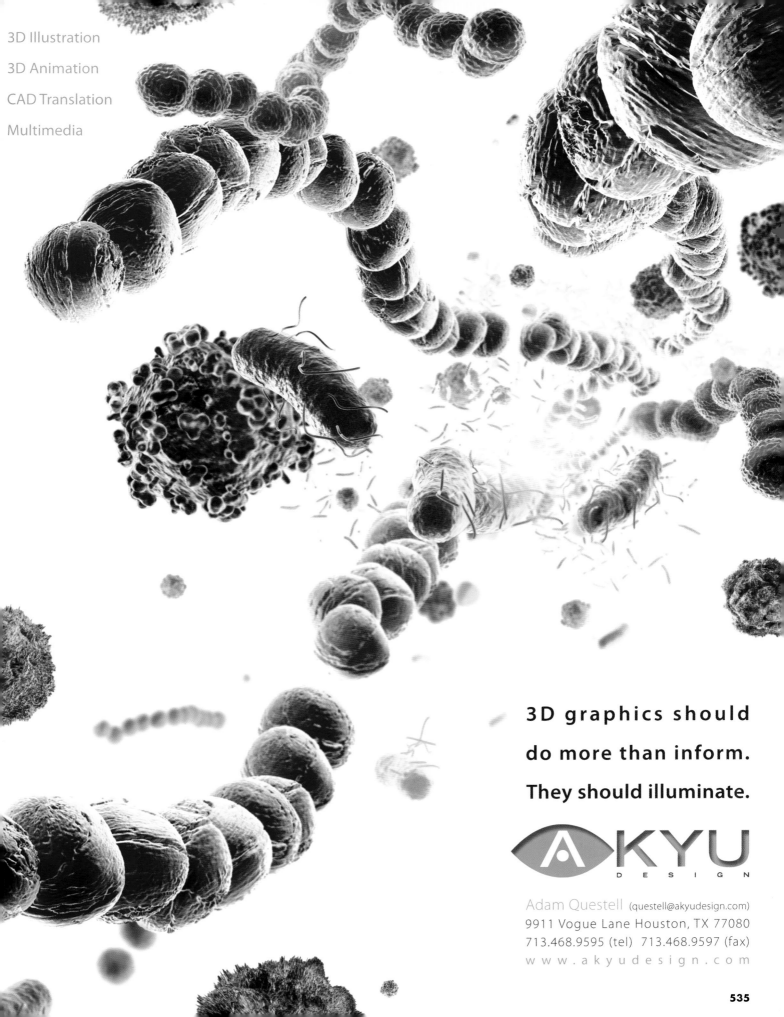

STEAK ESCAPE

ECLIPSE DESIGN GROUP

CYNDIE WIDMER | 301.570.1170

e c l i p s e d e s i g n g r o u p . c o m

illustration | photo illustration | icons | logos

DANIELLE CRISWELL

http://daniellecriswell.com
danielle.criswell@gmail.com   201-741-5829

MICHAEL FLEMING

illustration and character design

www.tweedlebop.com
510-292-4784
tweedlebop@gmail.com

Matthew Holmes · Artist
4760 American River Drive
Carmichael, CA 95608

916-971-4727
matthewholmes@att.net

Tantalizing Take Off

BATTLEGROUND STUDIO .com

WILLIAM BORDE
☎ **626.536.5810**
email: artcorp@earthlink.net

DAN PANOSIAN
PANAGRAPHICS

Broan

ShopRite

RedPrairie

ShopRite

Mark Bremmer
www.MarkBremmer.com
303-932-8759

KEITH · WARD

keith@wardillustration.com
www.wardillustration.com
414.943.9909

Michael Krider

voice **(800) 557-6206**
ACCESS CODE ➤ **06**

all original, all digital illustration | worldwide web **www.michaelkrider.com** | electronic mail **info@michaelkrider.com**

Digital Art for Web & Print!

Or call my mobile cellular phone... (504) 621-9301

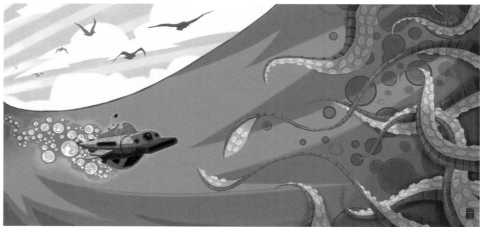

Tim Heitz
314.757.7103
spguy_25@yahoo.com
www.timheitz.blogspot.com

MIRACLE  STUDIOS
tm

FLASH ANIMATION • COMIC ART
CHARACTER DESIGN • MANGA
DIGITAL PAINTING • STORYBOARDS
ANIMATICS • COMIC BOOKS
CONCEPT ART • COPYWRITING
WEBISODES • GRAPHIC NOVELS
ONLINE GAMES • POP ART

SHAUNNA PETERSON
www.shaunnapeterson.com
(909) 205-6700
· ·

avier Medellin Puyou

011 (52) 444 4117 9588
mail@jilipollo.com
www.jilipollo.com

s. michelle **wiggins**
wigginsdesignstudio@yahoo.com   212-348-9341

S Michelle Wiggins

Sabai - Drinks brand illustration
Client: CookChick. UK

Ewart - Identity icon
Client: Elm House Creative. N Ireland

Asia Pacific - Identity icon
Client: Idea Brand Design. Oz

Irwin's Breads - Brand icon
Client: AV Browne. N Ireland.

SANDEMAN
ESTD. 1790

Sandeman: Brand icon
Client: Wren & Rowe. UK

Zebra PR - Identity icon
Client: Design Stable. UK

Lamb's Spiced Rum - Brand icon
Client: Elmwood Design. UK

CARLING

Carling
Global beer brand icon.
Client: Landor. UK

epicicons
by
CHRIS MITCHELL
ILLUSTRATIVE GLOBAL BRANDS

Hasting Hotels - Identity icon
Client: AV Browne. N Ireland

Food brand icon
Client: Ziggurat. UK

T/F + 44 (0) 1243 572 099
M + 44 (0) 7802 874 349
E chris@epicicons.com
W www.epicicons.com

Joan Reilly

illustration@joanreilly.com
www.joanreilly.com
(917) 543-6327

The Xenarthrans

xenarthran: mammal (magnorder Xenarthra): An ancient lineage of mammals comprising the armadillos (order Cingulata) and the sloths and anteaters (order Pilosa). The namesake feature shared by all members of Xenarthra is seen in the lower backbone. The lumbar vertebrae are "xenarthrous"; that is, they have extra contacts (joints, or arthroses) that function to strengthen the lower back and hips. This aids use of the forelegs in activities not associated with locomotion, such as digging——the primary method used by anteaters and armadillos to obtain food.   —*Encyclopaedia Britannica*

Hot Stuff

PENNAN Ink. presents Illustrations by TOM

Tom Milutinovic

www.CARTOONISTSonline.com

KINGPEN@CartoonistsOnline.com

403-247-2286

RANDY JONES

randyjones1@earthlink.net
randyjonesart.com
212.677.5387

GEORGE CARLIN

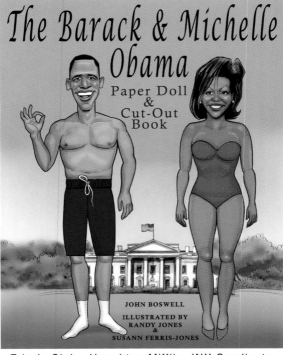

Clients include: Barron's, Brooklyn Public Library, Cambridge University Press, Friar's Club, Houghton Mifflin, INX Syndicate, The New York Times, Now What Media, and St. Martin's Press.

SUSANN FERRIS-JONES

susannferrisjones@earthlink.net
susannferrisjonesart.com
212.677.5387

Clients Include: Broadway Books, Cambridge University Press, Crown Publishing, Houghton Mifflin, Random House, St. Martin's Press, and Sterling Publishing.

JOHN CORKERY

www.mecha-mecha.com • 443-416-6327

DAVID HELFREY

503.287.8353 • davehelfrey.com

print • web • character design • accident-free for 16 days

harriet golden

www.harrietgolden.com   212.249.4194   harrietgolden@gmail.com

FASHION CAMP

DENNIS CLOUSE
WWW.CYCLONE-DESIGN.COM 206·323·7357

Michael Leu

illustration of fancy cats / landscape / serigraphs

415 - 706 - 6690   michaelleu@comcast.net   www.michaelleu.com

CHRIS
VAN ES

416-466-0288

POLITICS

Chris van Es Illustration
cvei@rogers.com
chrisvanes.com

EDUCATION

FINANCE

BUSINESS

HEALTH

Clients include: Washington Post, Chicago Tribune, Boston Globe, LA Times, Philadelphia Enquirer, Cleveland Plain Dealer, San Francisco Chronicle, World Watch Institute, Houston Chronicle, Dallas Morning News, Toronto Star, Hartford Courant, Christian Science Monitor, Medical Post, Heart & Soul, Saturday Night Magazine, Toronto Life, Bozell, Saatchi and Saatchi.

Thomas W. Schaller

los angeles, ca. usa
phone: 310.390.4630
info@twschaller.com
www.twschaller.com

architectural and fine arts in watercolor

cabo; mexico - 2008

st. christopher's; siena - 2009

Karen C. Rhine

Beauty of Wine Artist

*Specializing in
Commissions, Licensing
Commercial Products and Decor*

kcrhine@yahoo.com   www.beautyofwine.com   312.305.4610

BOOK COVERS

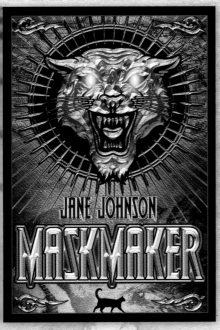

JANE JOHNSON
MASKMAKER

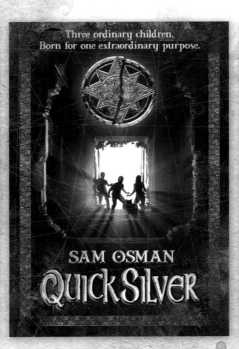

Three ordinary children.
Born for one extraordinary purpose.

SAM OSMAN
QUICKSILVER

CRUSADE

TWO BOYS
TWO FAITHS
ONE UNHOLY WAR

ELIZABETH LAIR

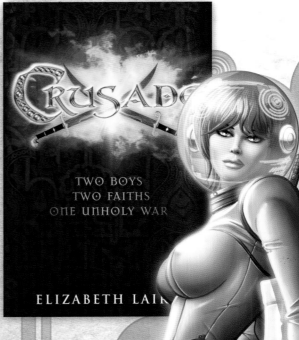

PINUPS

老実 武

THE ART OF EAMON O'DONOGHUE

CONTACT: (+44) 2380710328 • (+44) 7729482562 • EAMON@THEEXTREMIST.CO.UK • WWW.THEEXTREMIST.CO.UK

PROBLEM client lost market share in the international aquafeeds industry

SOLVED

created a series of friendly
characters to restore the
client's brand recognition
and put them back on top

Learn more, see more

GERBER STUDIO

Tradigital Illustration
mgerber@gerberstudio.com
www.gerberstudio.com
(203) 775-3658

LE CINEMA FRANÇAIS

MICHEL CIMENT
NICOLAS KLOTZ
CATHERINE BREILLAT
JEAN-MICHEL FRODON
EUGENE GREEN
AGNES VARDA

THE LEGACY OF 68

Relax & MOVE to the COUNTRY

WATCH this SPACE

Later I understood what seized my IMAGINATION that day

HOW STRANGE IT WAS TO SEE MEN DO SOMETHING BEAUTIFUL

 Andy Smith   web:www.asmithillustration.com   email: andy@asmithillustration.com   cell:+44(0)7949 997978

LEE COREY

© CoreyToons

 COREY TOONS

illustration   character development   animation   cartoons

web: **coreytoons.com**   email: **studio@coreytoons.com**   Tel: 845-613-7088

Illustrator
MARC GABBANA   www.marcgabbana.com   creator@marcgabbana.com   415 710 5358
Concept Artist

FRANK.VITALE
ILLUSTRATION.ANIMATION.VISUALIZATION
GAME DESIGN.VISUAL EFFECTS

MECHANICAL.WOLF ROCKFORD.FOSGATE

TEST.DRIVE.UNLIMITED ATARI

MECHANICAL.SCORPION ROCKFORD.FOSGATE

WOLF.CITY ROCKFORD.FOSGATE

TRANSFORMER HASBRO

PUNCH.AND.CHOPPER.SNOWBOARDS BURTON

THE.ENTRANCE PERSONAL

Yana Beylinson

www.yanabeylinson.com
ybeylins@gmail.com
917.319.0413

Award winning designer and illustrator;
skill set includes oil and acrylic painting,
pen and ink technique,
complex digital rendering,
logo design and branding.

Some clients: Shikatani Lacroix,
Grand Central Publishing, Macy's, Coach,
Mana Mind and Body, Mastercard,
Orange Coast Magazine,
Comptoir Sud Pacific.

Advertising • Design • Publishing

FARESTART PRESENTS THE 2009
Guest Chef on the Waterfront
Savor Tastes from Over 50 of the Area's Most Talented Chefs, Wineries and Purveyors of Fine Foods

CELEBRATING WASHINGTON'S LEADING CHEFS
See the full list of the amazing participants at www.farestart.org
Wednesday, July 15 • 6–9pm • Elliott Hall, Pier 66 • 21+ Event
Tickets: $60 Early-Bird before 6/1 $70 After 6/1 • Purchase at www.farestart.org or call 206.267.6223

RHONE RANGERS • The Mountain 103.7FM • BELL HARBOR INTERNATIONAL Conference Center • seattle • tp

FareStart
Great Food. Better Lives.

Poster design & illustration David Calkins – www.calkonia.com

© Expedia, Inc.

Partial Client List

Expedia, Inc

The Seattle Weekly

Beam Global Spirits & Wine

FareStart

The Sneakery

Everyman Theatre

206.303.8478 • david@calkonia.com

DOUG

TALALLA

STORYBOARDS

COMPS

ETC.

TALALLABAY.COM

612-

251-

3443

Detail from the 82 inch long
"Horizon" created for
Merrick / Towle Communications
Edwin Jenkins, Designer

Inside front cover
La Bella Lingua by Diana Hales
Broadway Books /
Random House

Yankee Magazine
New England's 25 Best
Places to Eat

Alabama Jazz Hall of Fame

RAYNE BEAUDOIN ILLUSTRATION

Tel: (206) 463-2607
23309 Wax Orchard Rd SW, Vashon Island, WA 98070
See more work online at www.raynebeaudoin.com

586

JEFF MULAWKA

www.jeffmulawka.com | 519·719·8212 | jeffmulawka@hotmail.com

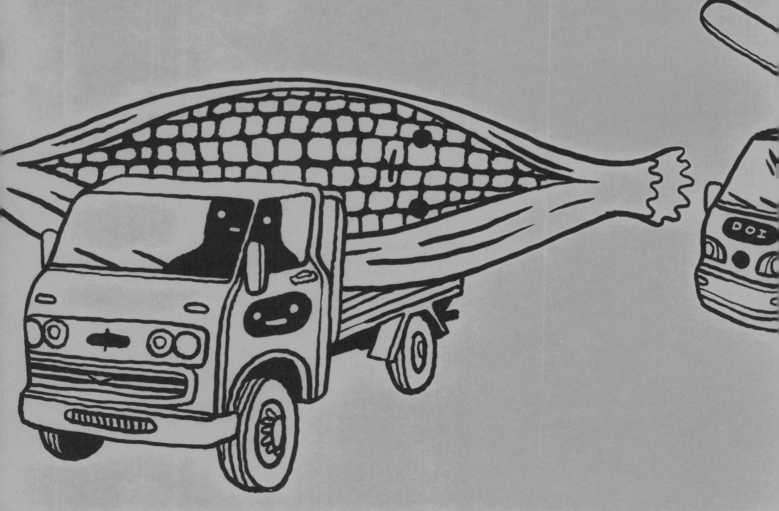